Jitterbug's Gift

Jitterbug's Gift

Lessons for Life

Robert C. Steiner

Copyright © 2018 by Robert C. Steiner

ISBN: 978-0-9748292-0-3
Library of Congress Control Number: 2003099651

Printed in the United States of America

For additional copies or information contact:
Robert C Steiner
Bobby@BobbySteiner.com

All rights reserved. No part of this book may be reproduced or transmitted in any form by any means, electronic or mechanical, including photocopying and recording, or by any information storage or retrieval system, except as may be expressly permitted by the 1976 Copyright Act or in writing by the publisher. While the lessons herein are real, the characters and accounts are fictional. Any similarities in name or place are coincidental. Furthermore, any slights against people, clubs, or organizations are unintentional.

Table of Contents

Introductions

If we are lucky, we encounter one person who has the power to change the course of our lives. If by some miracle there are several, we can say we are truly blessed. I, for one, had the good fortune and blessing of several great mentors in my life...many on par with the unique characters in this book that Bobby Steiner has so skillfully written about with great affection.

It has often been said golf imitates life, and Steiner has done a magnificent job of intertwining both the great nuances and secrets of the game with the power and mystery of love and friendships that know no boundaries.

While reading *Jitterbug's Gift*, I was moved by the same emotions I felt as a young man striving to reach my dream of being a champion golfer while searching for the approval of those who meant the most to me. Like Bobby and so many like him, I was often confronted by skepticism and people whose judgmental attitudes made it more difficult to stay focused on my dream. There were times when I felt so alone, fighting my fears, with doubt constantly bombarding my psyche. In the end, it was worth every drop of sweat and blood.

My father, rest his soul, once presented me with a clipping I cherished my entire competitive career – a quote from President Theodore Roosevelt. It is the one that begins with, "It's not the critic who counts." If you've not read it, I suggest you look it up. If you have read it, I suggest you refer to it often. Nothing captures the essence of courage quite like the words Roosevelt wrote more than a century ago. Bobby has that same kind of spirit and courage – we all should.

Being from the Deep South, Steiner and I also share a profound respect for the game of golf and the unique perspective of race, and its place in the history of the game. From the days of blacks picketing at Memorial Park in the early sixties because Charlie Sifford was denied a chance to play in the Houston Open, to my friend, Calvin Peete, winning the Tournament Players Championship; we have seen every possible scenario play out in the world of golf. Make no mistake, their contributions and the contributions of others like them have made the game better.

Jitterbug and Smiley are just two in a cast of thousands in our great game whose souls were touched by the hand of God. Despite a lifetime enduring prejudice, persecution, and hatred, they found a way to impact golfers of every race, young and old, with their wisdom, humor, and humility. Isn't that what life should be all about? I think so.

I congratulate Bobby Steiner on writing *Jitterbug's Gift*. As a good friend and colleague, Mike LaBauve, once said about Steiner's previous book, *Munie*, "You'll learn without being taught." It takes a special talent to achieve that goal, and Steiner has done it beautifully with *Jitterbug's Gift*.

Bill Pelham
Author of *Burke and Demaret*
Former PGA Tour Player

*****

Bobby Steiner is a one of a kind golf instructor, largely thanks to the colorful and amazingly talented cast of characters who taught him the game. He is also a fine storyteller. He blends his lessons so seamlessly through his plotlines you can often digest them without realizing you've been taught.

Weaving golf lessons stealthily throughout an entire novel takes a very special skill. Such is the case in *Jitterbug's Gift*, as well as Steiner's prior works. All of them contain a treasure trove of unique golf knowledge, the sort of help invaluable to serious beginners, as well as seasoned experts, looking to review critical elements of the game.

Beyond golf instruction, his stories provide subtle insights regarding pivotal life decisions. Best of all, the book is a fun read, an absolute must for golfers and anyone looking for a thoughtful story of overcoming obstacles and following dreams.

John Laubhan
Author of *True Sport* and *Bogeymen*

Prologue

Jitterbug once told me, "How you play the game shows something of your character; how you lose reveals the rest."

To say Jitterbug taught me golf is to leave a great deal out. He taught me as much about life; or, inspired me to teach myself. When I think of Jitterbug, he often brings to mind a character who might be most brilliantly played by Morgan Freeman. It wasn't so much his appearance; but rather, the calm, quiet certainty with which he conducted himself, whether shooting sixty-four. . . or seventy-four.

Jitterbug and I played in our usual, early morning tee time the day after I received my letter of acceptance into the Golf Professional's Training Program; something I dreamed of, worked toward, and looked forward to long before anybody thought I could do it. . . except for Jitterbug. I could hardly wait to share the details of my next big step with the man who, for reasons I never quite understood, gave so much of himself to see to it the path I traveled would lead to success.

Just as we were about to go out as a twosome, and before I could give Jitterbug the exciting news, a young lady came walking down to the tee. We welcomed her in and she introduced herself as Jenny.

After watching us tee off, I could tell Jenny was nervous.

"Guys, I'm not that good. I sure hope you're patient," she said. We encouraged her to relax and take her time. Jenny took a practice swing before dribbling her drive some thirty feet, barely clearing the teeing ground. "Whoops! Sorry guys. Look, if there's something I'm not doing right, feel free to tell me."

That was all I needed to hear. This was my chance to show Jitterbug how far I'd come. Jenny appeared to be athletic, and I knew I could sort her troubles out in a matter of seconds.

I started with her grip. After that, I corrected her posture, ball position, alignment, pivot, weight transfer, forearm rotation, and finish. But, it didn't matter what I said, for fourteen painful holes Jenny didn't get a single ball in the air. The more I asked her to relax, the tighter she held the club.

After hitting our tee shots at the par three fifteenth hole, Jitterbug stood, fixed in place, as Jenny made her way to the forward tee.

"What are you waiting for?" I asked.

"I'm waiting for you to take the handcuffs off that young lady."

I didn't know what he meant. "Handcuffs? What's that mean? She asked for help on the first tee."

"You're exactly right, Bobby. She asked for help on the first tee. And, unless I missed something, that's the last time the dear lady was given a chance to speak."

Jenny arrived at her tee before looking back to ours. "Okay. Now what?" she asked, expecting the barrage of instruction to continue.

Not sure what to say, I looked at Jitterbug who suddenly took on a different demeanor.

Smiling, he said, "I think Bobby finally figured out what's wrong, Jenny. If you don't mind, Bobby, I'll tell her what you told me."

Before I could think of what to say, he'd walked over to join Jenny. "What other games have you played before?"

She answered, "Well, softball, and..."

"Softball? Perfect! Let me see you swing that club like you were swingin' at a softball."

Jenny took a swing as if reacting to a pitch down the middle of the strike zone.

"Wonderful!" Jitterbug said. "You must've been a good hitter!"

"Better hitter than golfer, that's for sure," Jenny replied.

Jitterbug smiled. "Jenny, I want to see you swing again. Except, this time, show me how you'd hit a softball if the pitch was coming in around your ankles, just barely above home plate."

Jenny tilted beautifully, took the club back with poise and grace, and swung freely all the way to a complete finish. She ended in perfect balance, as if imagining the line-drive she'd driven deep to center field.

Jitterbug took a ball out of his pocket and placed it on a tee. "Here, Jenny, hit this low pitch," he said.

Things suddenly changed. Her white knuckles turned pink as she loosened her grip. Her arms hung freely. She stayed steady as she turned away from the ball, and returned to impact with the explosive combination of power and clubface, neither of which she'd successfully delivered all day. Her ball took off as if shot from a cannon, climbed high, and finally dropped, landing softly on the front edge of the green.

She looked at Jitterbug as if he'd returned her lost child. Before she could say anything, Jitterbug said, "You were right, Bobby. I didn't think so at first, but you were right. You figured out the solution." He then turned to Jenny. "Now, Jenny, just remember to hit that low pitch for the rest of the day and you can work on all that other stuff when you have the time to practice."

When Jenny was no longer in earshot, I said, "Jitterbug, I suppose the lesson here is I was talking when I should have been listening."

Jitterbug put his bag down next to the fifteenth green. "Oh,

I don't know," he said. "Maybe you were just too busy tellin' her stuff to ever think about askin' her anything." Jitterbug pulled the putter from his bag, took his glove off, and began the short walk to mark his ball. "But, I wouldn't worry too much about it," he said. "A guy can't figure out the right way unless he knows all about the wrong way."

Jenny finished her round with the confidence she could play golf, and I, reminded of what I'd always known – that Jitterbug is a true mentor, a man with whom I will always be proud to walk the fairway.

Let me tell you how it all happened...

Chapter One

You can do anything you want, but you can't do everything you want. You have to decide what's worth your commitment, and then give it your all.
– Jitterbug Bell

Carrie

With one week remaining before her scheduled departure, Carrie took me by the hand to share her vision of our future together.

"Oh Bobby, we have so many beautiful memories to be thankful for. But, with all the miles we'll soon find between us, it's better if we just make a clean break. I'm sorry, and it hurts to say that, but it's the right thing to do."

My greatest fear – a near-constant source of worry since the day Carrie signed her letter of intent – had come true. "Can't we at least try? I mean, we just have to stay committed; time will go by fast, you'll be home for summer, and before you know it..."

"Don't make this harder than it already is, Bobby. It's time we both move on."

Pleading proved futile; her mind was made up, and nothing I said would change it. Carrie would be gone soon, off on a life-changing adventure, and I was not to follow. Three years and seven months, countless first love experiences, all leading to heartache beyond anything I'd ever imagined.

The day Carrie left for school, Thursday, August 20, 1992, is a day I stayed in my room, too grief-stricken to be seen.

I had to get out of southern Indiana.

Jake

Jake put his tray down and slid into the middle of the booth. "So, what's your plan, Bobby?"

"What do you mean?"

"I mean what are you gonna do in North Carolina?"

"I'm making a change, Jake," I said. "I'm moving on."

Jake shook his head. "You're movin' backwards. Look, if you stick around here and make good of yourself, another girl will come along, and you'll forget all about Carrie."

"I just lost the girl I thought I'd marry. Everywhere I look reminds me of her. I don't want to be here anymore."

"Okay, then I'll ask again. What are you gonna do in North Carolina?"

"Don't take this the wrong way, Jake; I mean, you've been a good friend and all, but. . . you'll shoot me down."

"I'm not gonna shoot you down! Why would I care? Just tell me."

"Alright, since you must know, I'm gonna work on my golf game," I said.

Jake stared across at me blankly. "Congratulations, that's great. I'm gonna work on my golf game, too. But, I mean what are you gonna do for a living?"

"That's what I'm telling you. I'm gonna be a golf professional."

"Uh-huh, I see. Now, I probably already know the answer to this, but I'll ask anyway. Where'd you get this idea?"

"It's because of Carrie."

Jake nodded. "Of course it is."

"Look Jake, watching Carrie swing a golf club was the most beautiful thing I ever saw, and I've been hooked on the game since the first time she took me out to play. I just fell in love with it."

"And, so I can understand this, Bobby, what part of that story qualifies you to be a golf professional?"

"It doesn't, but just give me a second. Carrie is playing college golf now, so rather than stay here..."

"I know about Carrie's scholarship, Bobby. Everybody in town knows about it; she got a full ride, Tulane University, playing golf. . . which means she's gone now. Why are you torturing yourself with all this..."

"Will you let me finish? What I was saying is, rather than stay here and do nothing, I'm going to North Carolina to work on my golf game. My mom lives in Asheville, so I'll stay with her until I get on my feet. Once my game gets to pro level, there's three years of schooling to get PGA certified. Fast forward a few years, and Carrie and I will both be accomplished golfers, and both will have gone to school for it."

"And, let me guess. After all that, Carrie will want you back. Is that how this story ends? Is that really what you think?"

"Maybe, maybe not," I said. "But, she'll know what I did. She'll know I chased a dream, that I worked hard, and that I succeeded. And, she'll know I don't work in the plastics factory anymore. Even if I don't get her back, if she knows all that, it'll have to be good enough."

"Bobby, I have to be honest with you. Golf isn't the kind of game you can pick up at twenty years old and expect to be a professional. Imagine trying to do that with football or basketball. That would seem impossible, right? Well, golf is even harder."

"If I believed that then you'd be right."

"But, you never played any other sports, Bobby. How can you possibly..."

"I played sports. Just not since you've known me."

"Yeah, and I've known you since the seventh grade. Oh, wait, I forgot you used to be good at baseball. Way back in the first and second grade, before anybody knew you..." Jake stopped himself, looked down, and softened his tone. "I'm sorry, Bobby. I'm not trying shoot you down. Anyway, tell me, what's your game like now? Have you shot below, say. . . a hundred?"

"Not yet."

"How about a hundred and ten?"

"Twice."

Jake feigned enthusiasm. "Okay, that's a good start. How do you plan to make a living while you're working on your game?"

"I'll get a job at a golf course," I said. "I'll play every day before and after work."

Jake shook his head. "That's no good, Bobby. What about the winter time when it gets dark at five o'clock? You wouldn't get to play at all; and, even in the summer you'd only get in four or five hours. That's not workin' at golf. That's just bein' a golfer."

"Don't ruin this for me, Jake."

"I'm not tryin' to ruin it! I'm just saying you gotta come up with some other plan. Working at a golf course is not the same thing as working on your golf game."

We finished our breakfast, stacked our trays, and made our way out to the parking lot. "You'll be sure to call me if you come back around, won't you, Bobby?"

"Of course, Jake. You know I will."

"Best of luck, my friend."

The Lonely Road

My resolve grew stronger with every passing mile marker.

I have to get a night job. Jake is right, I can't work at a golf course. I need my days free to play golf.

After that, I have to find a place I can afford to play.

I already knew what was required to become a PGA Professional, as our local pro, Andy Earl, and I discussed it one rainy afternoon in the pro shop.

There are two parts to it. First, a thirty-six hole playing test, which requires a score of something close to par. Once the test is out of the way a guy can start the second part, a three-year training program.

Time to give this some perspective. On a scale of one to ten, my game needs to be a ten to pass, and I'm probably a strong one, or at best, a weak two. That's okay; four months ago I wasn't even on the chart.

I'll be twenty-one in a month. If it takes, say, six years to pass the playing test, I'll be twenty-seven when I qualify. Add to it three years of training, and by the age of thirty I'll be a professional.

This won't be like baseball. It's up to me this time. I'll be good enough because I'll make myself good enough.

Chapter Two

The only thing that matters is your commitment.
You can't fake it, and it does little good to talk about it.
A thousand well saids don't equal a single well done.
– Jitterbug Bell

Mom

"Are you going back to school?" Mom asked, only moments after I arrived.

"Yes, Mom," I said. "I have a plan and it involves going back to school."

"How wonderful!" Mom exclaimed. "Tell me about it. When will you start?"

"Not for a while," I said. "I have to work on my golf game first."

"Your golf game?"

"Yes. That's my plan. I'm going to be a golf professional. Once my game gets to pro level I have three years of schooling to complete."

"Didn't you just start playing golf, Bobby?"

"Yes."

"And, you're going to be a professional?"

"Yes."

"Bobby, can you come sit next to me on the couch?"

I knew what that meant. I'd sat next to her on a different couch twelve years ago when she broke the news we'd be moving five hundred miles away from my father; and for the next four years, I would only see him at Christmas, and two weeks every summer.

"I'm not going to sit down, Mom; not if you're going to discourage me."

"Do you have any idea how ridiculous you sound?"

"Mom, please don't make this something we can't talk about."

"You're staying in my house, and we *will* talk about your plan for the future."

This was the last thing I needed. "Mom, I can't do regular college. You know how I was in school."

"If you spent half the time on your school work as you did your baseball books you would've been first in your class."

"Don't talk about my books!" Those words came out like a bolt of lightning, and with them came instant regret. "I'm sorry. I didn't mean to raise my voice."

Mom stared at me in silence, then nodded her head, and turned to walk back into the kitchen. Once out of my view, she finally spoke. "I didn't know that was still a sore subject."

"It's not, I'm sorry, I don't know why I yelled at you." I walked into the kitchen where Mom stood, staring out the sliding glass patio door. "But Mom, you have to understand those books were my passion. And, now my passion is golf. Please let me show you what I can do."

"We can talk about this later," she said. "What are you going to do for work?"

"I'll start looking today."

*****

I searched through the job postings in the classified ads; one in particular caught my eye. Within a week I'd landed a job as a server at a fine dining Italian restaurant, Ristorante da Vincenzo.

Being a waiter was nowhere near the top of my list, but I needed a job, and it had to be at night. I'd stick it out, do my best, and learn the trade.

Step one complete. I found a night job.

*****

It didn't take long to figure out my must-do-now list was missing an important step. I had to get my own place. Mom was loving, but the disappointment on her face when I talked about golf was more than I could stand. What's worse, my game showed minimal signs of improvement, which I didn't dare let Mom know. The only thing worse than beating the ball all over the course is having to come home and defend my right to continue the pursuit.

The first week of March, 1993, I moved into a run-down, one-bedroom apartment in West Asheville. It wasn't much, but it was mine, and I could double-bogey in relative peace.

Step two in the books. I have my own place.

Muni

By mid-May I'd saved enough tip money for a membership at Asheville Municipal Golf Course, a Donald Ross design affectionately known as "Muni."

The $250 it cost for a one-year membership at Muni wouldn't cover a single month at any other course. A few people around town called Muni the "black course," a reference to the number of African

Americans who played there. It was the one golf course out of dozens around western North Carolina to have always allowed African Americans to play. Or, at least that's what I heard. All I can say for sure is I felt at home at Muni, and never thought much about race, mine or anyone else's.

Having a membership meant I could walk the golf course all day for no extra charge. Riding in a cart seemed like an unnecessary luxury, one I couldn't afford, especially given the amount I played. If I had the night off from work, I could walk as many as fifty-four holes in a day. Sometimes I played by myself, but usually found some random person to tag along with. There were about ten guys like me, who played every day, so I got to know more than a few regulars. To me, Muni was a mountain, and I wanted to climb it as many times as possible.

Step three underway. I have a place to play.

Step four, the Player Ability Test, is somewhere, way off in the distance.

But, I'll get there.

Chapter Three

If you know you can chip, if you're confident you can chip,
if you plan to chip, you'll put a good swing on
every club in your bag, including your driver.
– Jitterbug Bell

Smiley Changed Everything

I remember it well, and can still recall nearly every detail. It was Sunday, the 6th day of June, 1993. Vincenzo's was closed on Sundays, so I could play golf until dark. I arrived at the tenth tee with what I figured to be forty minutes left of daylight, which meant I needed to hurry. I was the first person on the golf course, and planned to be the last.

It was hot and sticky out, but I played the tenth and eleventh holes in less than ten minutes, and began to wonder about the back nine record, time-wise that is. I hit a good tee shot on the par four twelfth hole, and dropped my bag when I reached my ball. What happened next would forever change the course of my golf studies.

I looked down the fairway and saw an African American man, small in stature, practicing chip after chip from in front of the twelfth green. He had his back to me, and I could tell he didn't expect anyone to be on the back nine so late in the evening.

I picked up my bag and dropped it again, hoping he'd hear me and move to the side so I could hit my approach. When he didn't so much as flinch I decided to forget it and move on to the thirteenth. I had to keep going if I had any hope of finishing before dark.

I threw my bag over my shoulder and hurried down the hill. The rattle of my clubs echoed in time with my quick, steady step. *I wonder if he can hear me now.* It didn't matter long, for what came into focus stopped me dead in my tracks.

It wasn't, as I thought, just a case of a man hitting chip shots close to a hole. Far more captivating was the manner in which he did so.

The first shot flew almost straight up, landed beyond the flag, and spun back to the hole. The next stayed low, took a single bounce and skidded to an abrupt halt. This pattern the little man repeated – one high, one low, all stopping within inches of the cup – until the scattered balls around his feet formed a bunched up pile around the flagstick.

Hoping not to startle him, I called out as I got nearer. "It looks like you're pretty good at that."

The little man looked up and I could see he was much older than I would've guessed. It seemed odd at first, as I'd never seen a person upon whom time had taken such a unique toll. The passing decades had hollowed his cheeks and turned his hair white, but kindly left alone his manner of movement.

"I'm Bobby," I said, offering my hand.

His gaze climbed to half-mast, and stayed in place long enough to shake my hand, but quickly returned to the empty shag bag at his feet. It occurred to me he hadn't invited me to join him, so I wished him a good evening and turned to make my way to the next tee. I hadn't made it far when I heard the first words of what was to become a lasting friendship.

"I been playin' this same wedge for over fifty years," he said.

Ecstatic that he spoke, I turned and replied, "Yeah, I can believe that. You seem reasonably familiar with it."

He looked me up and down. "You any good at chippin'?" I could feel my heart race as I reached for my wedge. "Nah, here, use this one," he said, handing me his old relic.

I took his wedge and wrapped my fingers around it. There was nothing about the club I found particularly user-friendly. It had an unfamiliar offset and needed a new grip. It even looked a little bent around the hosel, but I couldn't help but imagine it had a mind of its own.

I chipped a few balls in the direction of the hole. A couple rolled near the cup; one even threatened, but none had the look or sound of his. I knew then it wasn't the club.

"You got good hands," he said. "But your technique needs some work. You want some help?"

I couldn't believe this was happening. "Yes, of course; I mean, please."

He had me stand up to a ball as if preparing to hit a chip shot. "Lift ya right foot off the ground."

Not sure if this was some sort of instructional slang, I said, "I'm sorry, lift my foot. . . what?"

"Lift ya right foot off the ground and start chippin' some balls." I did as he said and it immediately changed everything. Although at first I struggled to keep my balance, the shots that followed were crisp beyond anything I'd felt before. He told me I should hit chip shots standing on one foot for the next week, and if I did he'd show me more.

"That means every single chip shot," he said. "And if I hear you been usin' two feet I ain't showin' you nothin' else. You got that?"

"Sure, but I didn't catch your name."

We again shook hands. "My name is Smiley. And I'll see you here next week."

"Right here?"

"That's where we at, ain't it? Right here, Sunday night, one week from now, just before dark. And you best remember, you chip one ball on two feet and there ain't no use in showin' back up. I'll know if you did or not."

Dark was falling fast, so I said good-bye and walked the road back to the clubhouse. Excited by the experience, I almost forgot I'd been carrying my clubs around the golf course for most of the last thirteen hours. I'd had my first encounter with someone who was willing to help me. I couldn't wait to see him again.

The None-To-None Shot

I returned exactly one week later. As promised Smiley was waiting for me in front of the twelfth green with a small pile of balls at his feet.

"Well, I did what you said. I've been practicing chip shots without even once letting my right foot touch the ground."

"You learn anything?"

Indeed I had. For a whole week I'd stayed away from actually playing golf, choosing instead to hit chip after chip while standing on just my left foot. And, never before had chipping been so easy. If Smiley had nothing else to teach me he'd already given me the most worthwhile piece of advice to date.

"I learned that I don't need my right foot to hit a good chip shot. And, for that matter, I found out it doesn't take long to develop touch around the green."

"Develop? Shoot! Ain't nobody gotta develop no touch. If you can throw a ball to someone standin' ten feet away you got enough touch to hit a good chip shot. The problem is that people sway back and forth when they chip so they never make decent contact with the ball. But bein' on one foot makes it impossible to sway. You either gotta stay still or fall over. Anybody can chip when they don't sway."

"Why didn't you just tell me not to sway then?"

"'Cause you can't feel it when it happens!" Smiley exclaimed. "You'd stop swayin' for a shot or two, and then say, 'Oh, I got it now,' and then forget all about it. Sometime later you'd start hittin' bad chips again and blame it on somethin' else besides the sway. That's the reason people don't never get no better. Hittin' a couple good shots is all it takes to make a guy forget what he's supposed to be workin' on. You gotta practice long past the point where you think you got it. You have to ingrain it, and that's why I had you spend a week on just ya left foot."

Smiley told me to take my normal stance and chip some balls for him. Though I put my right foot back on the ground, the urge was to load most of my weight on the left foot.

"That means we're good on stayin' steady," Smiley said. "So, next is hand action. You gotta learn the 'none-to-none' shot."

"What do you mean, 'none'?"

"That's how much wrist action you use," Smiley replied. "On a short little chip shot you use a none-to-none, which means no wrist action on the back swing, and *none* on the way through."

Smiley demonstrated the movement, then told me to try it. I positioned my club behind a ball and was about to hit a shot when Smiley knocked the ball away from my club. "No ball," he said. "Just make the motion."

Smiley watched me swing back and forth in a none-to-none motion for what seemed like a hundred swings, never looking away from my hands. "You think you can practice this on your own?"

"I'm sure I can." I placed my club behind a ball and was about to hit when Smiley, once again, knocked the ball away. "No balls for a week."

"What do you mean, 'no balls'?"

"I'll tell ya what I mean, you gonna dry swing for a week. That's what I mean. You gotta learn to swing without using any wrist action on the way through the chip shot. I'd say one week oughtta be enough, unless it turns out you need longer than that."

I wanted to try it on a ball. In what must have sounded like a desperate plea, I said, "Wouldn't it be more helpful to practice with a ball? I can just make sure I don't get wristy. I'll keep an eye on it."

"Oh, I'm sorry!" Smiley exclaimed. "But I thought you was lookin' for some help. I won't make that mistake again! You can do it however you want."

"All right," I conceded. "I'll dry swing for as long as you'd like."

Smiley walked toward me with a look that told me it was time to listen. "Bobby, can't nobody ever get command over the short shots until they learn to move through impact without flippin' they wrists at the ball. For now, a ball sittin' there is just gonna make you wanna flip your wrists, 'cause that's what a beginner's mind says they have to do to get the ball in the air. Dry swingin' is the only way to get rid of the flip."

"I understand," I said, although I was sure it didn't matter.

"Good. Now, I think one week will be long enough."

"So, I'll meet you back here in a week then?" I asked, dejected.

"Yes sir!" Smiley replied with the first I'd seen of a genuine twinkle in his eye. "And come early 'cause I'm gonna have a surprise for you."

I didn't doubt for a minute he'd have a surprise for me. I walked back to my car thinking how fortunate I was to have met Smiley. Maybe his approach was a little extreme, but so was my desire. Whatever he had in store, I'd be there early the next week.

Chapter Three

Jessica

Walking in to work on Tuesday, two nights after my last visit with Smiley, I stopped by the hostess stand to find out what section of the restaurant I'd call home for the evening. Jessica was there, on the phone, taking a reservation. "Yes sir, that's correct," she said. "No sir, jackets are not required, but you are so good to ask! You're very welcome. See you at seven then. Bye-bye."

Jessica hung up the phone, marked the reservation sheet, and grabbed my forearm with a serious, down-to-business expression. "Do you see anything special about your station?"

I looked down at the seating chart. "I can see table forty-four is on hold for a 6:30 reservation."

"Yes, that's right. They wanted the most handsome server in the house. And, since Michael, Mike, and George are all off tonight. . ." Jessica stopped, turned, and gave me a smile.

Our lovely, young hostess was being playful, but I didn't want to linger too long. "I better go get my tables ready."

"Wait a minute! Don't you even want to know who you are waiting on at 6:30?"

"Do I know them?"

"Not yet," she said.

"Do YOU know them?"

Jessica did her best to fight back a smile. "Yes, I do," she said. "They're VIPs."

I leaned in for another peak at the reservation. "Carrington?"

"Yes, Dr. Carrington."

"VIPs?"

"Yes. Very important parents." I must've looked puzzled. "My parents. You're waiting on my parents. My last name is Carrington;

thank you for not knowing. They'll be here at 6:30. At table forty-four. Don't be late!"

I did my best to act excited. "That's great. I can't wait to meet them."

Jessica went on to tell me her father was a neurologist, and her mother, a school counselor. She lived with her parents during the summer, but would return to the University of North Carolina, Chapel Hill, in the fall. No stranger to the footlights, Jessica was a theater major.

Jessica appeared in the kitchen at exactly 6:30. "They're here," she said.

I dropped a couple of salads off at another deuce, and made my way to table forty-four where Jessica was already fixed, waiting patiently for my arrival. "Mom, Dad, this is Bobby."

Jessica's father spoke first. "It's great to actually get to meet you," he said.

Actually meet me? What's that mean? "Thank you. It's a pleasure to have you here."

Dinner came off without a hitch. I put in their dessert order and returned to the table with coffee. Jessica's father looked up. "I understand you play golf," he said.

I nodded. "Yes sir, I do."

Dr. Carrington sat up in his chair. "Call me Roger."

"And, I'm Margaret," Mrs. Carrington said.

Roger moved his coffee cup to the edge of the table. "You know, Bobby, we happen to be members at Cambria Country Club. Have you ever played there?"

"No I haven't, but I understand it's very nice."

"Yes it is. Maybe some time I can have you out to play golf. You think you could find the time?"

Why would he want to play with me? "Yeah, I'd like that, but are you sure you want to play with me? I'm not that good yet."

Roger paused, seemingly bewildered, then let out a big laugh. "I'm not falling for that!" he said. "Jessica already told me you're on your way to being a pro. I'm not going to be your sucker."

What? I didn't tell Jessica I was good at golf. Why would she tell her dad that?

Margaret gave her husband a tap on the forearm. "Honey, aren't you free tomorrow?"

Roger took a moment to consider it. "Yes, I'm on vacation this week. How about tomorrow?"

"Tomorrow? Uh, I guess I could play. Are you sure?"

"Of course, I'm sure. How does mid-morning sound?"

"That's fine," I said. "I'll go get your desserts. When I get back we can nail down a time."

Pushing open the kitchen door, reality smacked me in the face, as I remembered Smiley's words, "No balls for a week." *Just my luck.*

I tried to imagine how I could re-interpret Smiley's instructions, but could think of nothing unclear in his message. *If I want Smiley's help I have to do it his way. It's all or nothing.*

Desserts in hand, I inched back to the table. "I'm sorry, but something came up, and I can't play tomorrow."

"That's okay," Roger said. "I'm on vacation through Friday. Is there another day this week you'd like to play?"

"That's just it, I can't play this week at all. I promised my teacher I wouldn't hit any balls until I see him again on Sunday, and..."

"Hold on right there," Roger said. "Let me get this straight. Your teacher made you promise him you wouldn't hit any golf balls this week? That's why you can't play? And, here I thought I'd heard every excuse in the book, but that's a new one."

"That's not an excuse," I said. "I have to practice chipping without a ball for a whole week."

"Look, Bobby, if you were hoping to gamble, it's fine with me;

we can play for something small. But, if you think I'm just going to hand you my wallet, and let you take advantage of…"

"No, no!" I said. "I don't care about gambling. It's my teacher, I'm being honest. I can't hit balls this week." There was no way to explain Smiley in a way that would make sense.

"Where did you meet this teacher of yours?"

"On the twelfth green at Asheville Golf Course."

"You met your teacher at Muni? Jessica said you're a serious golfer, and you're telling me your teacher is from Muni?"

"My teacher doesn't actually work at Muni," I said. "At least not that I know of. It's kind of a long story."

"Maybe some other time then," Roger said. "I'm sorry your teacher won't let you hit balls this week. I hope it helps your golf game."

Yeah, me too.

Putting It Together

I forgot all about the surprise Smiley promised me until the moment I saw him the following Sunday. I'd been too busy fighting the urge to hit a golf ball to give it any thought. I'd done as assigned and spent a week rehearsing, in thin air, the none-to-none chipping motion Smiley showed me. And this, despite the enormous temptation to try it on a live round. Man I desperately wanted to hit a golf ball.

To add to the torture, I had to decline Jessica's Dad's offer to play Cambria Country Club. It was not easy; in fact, it was horrible, but I stood strong and dry swung in front of the living room mirror as I counted down the days.

When I neared the green that evening I could see Smiley wasn't alone. With him stood a tall, African American man with glasses, an athletic build, and a coolness I could sense before I got within a full wedge of him. He was much younger than Smiley; I figured somewhere close to fifty.

"Say hello to my nephew, Harold," Smiley said. "He gonna take a look at ya golf game."

The moment I saw Harold, I just knew he was *somebody*. His proud posture and staunch eye contact were intimidating, so I struggled for words when he extended his hand. "Pleased to meet you, Harold. But I don't have, well, I mean, I don't know how I can possibly pay you for..."

Smiley interrupted. "Harold got the course record here at Muni. Shot sixty-two on four different occasions from them back tees."

I was speechless. I wasn't sure I wanted Harold to look at my game. Heck, just a month ago I found myself in a trance-like state and somehow managed to string five pars together. But sixty-two? *What does sixty-two look like?*

"Let me see you chip a golf ball," Harold said, pointing to the flag near the middle of the green.

I started to mention not having hit a golf ball in seven days, but thought better of it. I didn't want to sound like an excuse maker. It was time to put my best foot forward and show I'd done my homework.

My hands shook visibly as I took the wedge out of my bag. With my clubface squarely behind a ball, I leaned my body toward the hole until there was no weight on my back foot. With the shaft of my wedge leaning left, I took the club away from the ball, and returned to impact in the same none-to-none motion I'd faithfully rehearsed for seven straight days.

Then it happened.

My wedge grabbed the ball, gave it a charge, and let it go with the combination of forward energy and drag spin. The shot raced up, but skidded to a dead stop with no more than two feet separating it from the edge of the cup. I'd chipped many as close, but never one that felt so well executed. It was in this moment I realized the golf club possessed intelligent design, and I'd never before used it properly. *The ball is not to be batted, as if with a croquet mallet. It's to be controlled with a mix of spin and velocity, something more akin to how a pool player commands a cue stick.*

I saw the way Smiley looked at Harold. It was as if he wanted to say, "I showed him how to do that." Harold looked at Smiley and then back at me. "How long you been playing?"

"About a year now."

"What are you trying to do with it?"

I reached deep within and somehow found the nerve to tell him the truth. "I'm going to be a professional."

Harold nodded his head, "Uh-huh, I see," he said. "I guess you know that's a pretty lofty goal. Do you have any idea how much work that will take?"

"Yes, sir."

"Oh yeah? The whole world is going to tell you that you started too late, that your goal is unrealistic. Are you gonna let that bother you?"

I shook my head. "I've already heard all that. I don't care."

"Are you gonna do like everybody suggests and quit after a couple of years?"

"No way."

Harold looked me straight in the eye for what seemed like an eternity. "I'm teeing off tomorrow morning at seven. Any chance you can meet me on the first tee?"

With what remained of my composure, I nodded and replied, "Yes sir, I can be there."

Harold extended his hand with the same warm, put-you-at-ease smile I've since seen a million times. "And no more of this 'sir' stuff either. My friends call me Jitterbug. I'll see you bright and early."

The Some-To-None Shot

I arrived early the next morning for my seven o'clock meeting, and found Jitterbug practicing chips to the makeshift short-game green. It didn't take long to see that Jitterbug, like Smiley, possessed deft touch with a wedge in his hand. I called out, "Is that the none-to-none chip shot?"

Without looking up, Jitterbug replied, "Nope, I don't use the none-to-none shot."

I was confused. Had Smiley thought so much of me he'd shown me something that even Jitterbug didn't know about? "Nah, I'd say I haven't used that old none-to-none shot in at least forty years," he said. "You'll never get good chipping that way."

"Well, then why did Smiley make me spend a whole week practicing it? Doesn't he know what he's talking about?"

Jitterbug smiled as he looked up to answer. "Now, hang on a minute," he said. "I had to learn the same thing when I started. And only after I could do the none-to-none motion perfectly did Smiley teach me the 'some-to-none' shot. And that's how I've chipped ever since."

"What's the 'some'-to-none shot?"

He asked me in return, "Well, what's the 'none'-to-none shot?"

As much time as I'd spent practicing the none-to-none, I could tell him anything he wanted to know about it. "The none-to-none," I said, "is a chip shot with no wrist action in the backswing and *none* on the way through impact. A perfectly wrist-less chipping motion."

"If that's true," Jitterbug said, "what do you suppose a some-to-none is?"

I thought it through before replying, "Well, that would be *some* wrist action on the backswing and *none* on the way through."

"That's right! And that's the way great chippers, including Smiley, hit their chip shots."

He gave me a moment to think about it before continuing. "See, in order to play all the different shots around the green, you have to be able to vary how high your chip shots fly; in other words, your trajectory. But to do that, you have to learn to set your wrists a little on the backswing."

"What do you mean, 'set' your wrists?"

"There's not a whole lot to it," Jitterbug said. "Just let your right wrist cup a little just as you change from backswing to downswing on the chip shot. Cupping your right wrist is the *some* part. Then, just keep the back of your right wrist cupped through impact. That's the *none* part. That's why it's a some-to-none shot."

"I see what you mean, but I chipped pretty well with the none-to-none."

Jitterbug nodded. "Well, now, the none-to-none is a shot you can play when you're within ten feet of the green and got a little room to run the ball. But what about when you're thirty feet away and the flag is cut close to the edge of the green? You're gonna need a little 'some' in your backswing to get the ball up so that it doesn't run past the hole. Besides that, letting your right wrist cup a little on the backswing will keep your motion from feeling so stiff and rigid."

"What about a *some-to-some*? Is there such thing a thing?"

Jitterbug shook his head. "You might as well forget about the some-to-some," he said. "That's not for you right now."

By this time, Jitterbug had his clubs over his shoulder and was on his way to the first tee.

"That's cool!" I said, struggling to catch up. "What other shots are you gonna teach me today?"

"Shots? You got plenty of time to think about shots. Today, we're just playin' golf."

Chapter Four

You have to play golf if you want to get better.
If you spend all your time on the range
that's where you'll hit your best shots.
– Mr. Vaughn

The Indian On The Hill

Already on the tee when we arrived were a young boy and his father. The boy's father invited Jitterbug and I to go on ahead of them.

"Why don't we all play together?" Jitterbug said. "That way we can round out a foursome."

The boy's father shook his head. "Thanks, but we don't want to hold you up. This is Sammy's eighth birthday and his first day on a real golf course."

Jitterbug smiled at Sammy, who was obviously eager to play. "We're in no hurry. Tee it up, birthday boy."

Sammy teed his ball up and took a long, out-of-balance swing with his cut-down driver. The ball barely got airborne, and bounced along the ground before getting caught up in the tall grass just short of the fairway. Little Sammy spun out, almost toppling over at his finish. "Ah, man!" he bemoaned. "I knew I'd mess up!"

Sammy's father teed off next. He hit a good drive, fairly long and down the left center of the fairway. Jitterbug motioned for me to go next. I felt like a big bundle of pent up, nervous energy as my weak fade came to rest in the long grass bordering the trees on the right side.

I turned and watched in great anticipation as Jitterbug put his tee in the ground. His beautifully efficient rhythm became evident as he glided through a rehearsal swing. I couldn't help but wonder, *How can it be I'm playing with the course record holder? Ten under par sixty-two on four different occasions. It's hard to believe a guy can play golf like that.*

It became easier to believe when Jitterbug squared up to hit his shot; he drew the club back effortlessly and finished his swing full and balanced. The ball sailed obediently down the center of the fairway, and returned to earth like a rock skipping across a pond. Jitterbug slowly bent over to pick up his tee.

At this, we all threw our clubs over our shoulders to make the walk down the first fairway. Before we stepped off the teeing ground, Jitterbug pointed to a nearby wooded mountainside. "Hey Sammy, you see that big hill over there?"

"Yes, sir."

"There's an old Indian who lives up there. He's looking down here watching us right now."

"Really?" the young boy lamented. "I hope he didn't see my shot."

Jitterbug looked around as if to make sure nobody was listening. "You know, Sammy, you can trick that old Indian. He's too far away to see where your ball goes, so as long as you keep your balance after you swing he'll think you hit a good shot." Jitterbug demonstrated what he meant.

Sammy stepped up to his ball with the iron Jitterbug had selected from the young boy's bag. Seemingly poised to play his shot, Sammy stole a quick peek at the hill, perhaps hoping to catch a glimpse of the old Indian. Young Sammy took a mighty cut, but rolled his topped iron shot some fifty yards down the fairway. Unshaken, the boy held his finish with a grace and balance to rival even Jitterbug. He coolly returned his club to his bag and without looking up asked, "Do you think the Indian saw that shot?"

Jitterbug assured him, "Oh, I bet he did. And he probably thinks you knocked it in the hole."

For the remainder of the round, Sammy steadily improved, faithfully holding his finish on every shot until he made his final putt.

One-To-One

In the clubhouse after our round, Jitterbug and I sat down for an iced tea and a moment to talk. "That was a lot of fun, Jitterbug. Thanks for playing with me."

Jitterbug looked up. "Oh good, I enjoyed it too, Bobby."

"That was really cool what you did for Sammy. I hate to admit it, but I stole the lesson you gave him and started holding my finish, too. It worked like magic. I just shot ninety-nine. My first time below a hundred."

"Congratulations!" Jitterbug said. "That's a good score. And, you're right, a balanced finish is like magic. It's the one thing every great player has in common. Not having a balanced finish is the one thing every bad player has in common. It's the least talked about, most important part of every great player's swing."

There was so much I wanted to know about Jitterbug. "How did you get so good at golf?"

Jitterbug laughed. "Well, thank you for that. My father passed away when I was eight. Uncle Smiley had just one son, my cousin, Hardpan, who was two years younger than me, so I moved in with them. I guess it's fair to say Hardpan and I, growing up, had a bit of a household rivalry, as far as golf goes. He's a pro now, and the best player you'll ever see. Smiley calls Hardpan his 'pro son,' and me, his 'amateur son,' even though I'm really just his nephew."

"And, what about Smiley?" I asked. "Is he a pro, too?"

"Nah, not at golf," Jitterbug said. "But, Smiley did play professional baseball in the 1930's. He was a shortstop. You probably never heard of Josh Gibson, but..."

I nearly jumped out of my seat. "Are you kidding me? I know everything about Josh Gibson. He played for the Homestead Grays, and hit over 800 home runs, more than any other player in history. They called him the 'Black Babe Ruth.' He died of a brain tumor when he was thirty-five. Did Smiley know Josh Gibson?"

Jitterbug seemed taken aback by my excitement. "Yes sir, Smiley played for the Homestead Grays. But he didn't just 'know' Josh Gibson. They traveled together and shared a room in every city. Josh was Smiley's best friend."

This is incredible. To think Smiley actually roomed with Josh Gibson. I never in my life thought I'd know somebody who played in the Negro Leagues.

"In fact, if you ever wonder how Smiley got his nickname, it was Josh Gibson who gave it to him. Josh called him Smiley because Uncle Smiley never smiled. So, it's a joke name, but it stuck, and Smiley has been introducing himself that way as long as I can remember. I bet if you asked him his real name it would take him a second or two to recall."

We both laughed. "Wait a minute," I said. "What was Smiley's full name when he played baseball?"

"Franklin," Jitterbug said. "Franklin Bell."

I thought about it for a moment. "You say, Franklin Bell? He's not related to Cool Papa Bell is he?"

"Yes, sir!" Jitterbug said, laughing in surprise. "That's my Uncle James, Smiley's older brother. He just passed away a couple of years ago. Now you tell me, Bobby, how in the world do you know about Cool Papa?"

This is surreal. "You're Cool Papa's nephew? He was one of the greatest players ever. He batted .337 lifetime, and stole 175 bases in 1933 alone. Satchel Paige said Cool Papa was so fast he could turn off the lights, and be in bed under the blankets before it got dark in the room. I can't believe he's your uncle. I'm sorry to hear he passed away."

"Thank you. It was a sad day. But, you didn't answer my question. How do you know so much about baseball? You must've been a ballplayer yourself."

I paused, unsure of what to say. My time in baseball wasn't a topic I was eager to discuss. "It's kind of a long story," I said. "I don't want to bore you with it."

"Well, I can't wait to tell Smiley," Jitterbug said. "That is, if it's okay with you. He'll be thrilled to know you pulled Cool Papa out of thin air."

"Yeah, tell him whatever you want," I said. "But, I'm curious, has Smiley been your teacher all these years?"

"No. Smiley's best friend, Mr. Vaughn, took over as my teacher the year after I moved in with Smiley; I've been workin' with Mr. Vaughn ever since."

Jitterbug just shot two under on the front nine and three under on the back. *What's he need a teacher for?*

"So anyway, I cut the grass here at Muni for thirty years," Jitterbug said. "I took a retirement from the city about six months ago, and now I'm just fishing and playing golf. I usually walk eighteen holes in the morning and finish by about ten o'clock. Then I have my whole day free to hang out with Smiley, or whittle away in my little woodshop or whatever. That way I can be there when my wife gets home from work around five."

"Who do you usually play with?"

"Whoever is standing there is who I play with," Jitterbug said. "Just like this morning. It's a good way to meet people. Of course, if you're ever up early feel free to join me."

"I can be here every morning," I said.

"Then I'm sure I will see you." At that, Jitterbug left to meet Smiley, and I, to play another eighteen holes. On the way past the counter, I checked with Stan Watkins, the pro shop attendant, to make sure it was okay for me to play.

"I think you can probably just head on down to the tee, Bobby," Stan said.

"Perfect, catch you later then."

Stan stopped me. "Say, did you play with Jitterbug this morning?"

"Yes I did."

"You know anything about Jitterbug?" I couldn't be sure where this was going. Stan was a retiree who worked at Muni a couple of days each week. I got the feeling it was just a way for him to pass time. He was missing a thumb and forefinger on his left hand, something I didn't know him well enough to ask about.

"I know he used to cut the grass here. Other than that, not really."

"Stay here a second." Stan turned and walked from behind the counter into the club repair room; and, returned a moment later holding a wooden plaque. "Look here," he said. "These are the past Muni club champions. Do you recognize any of these names?"

There, listed one by one, were the winners of every club championship between 1945 and 1974. Smiley won almost every year from 1947 to 1962, and Jitterbug won every year starting in 1966. "Wow, Smiley and Jitterbug used to win all the time."

"One of them still does," Stan said. "The last time somebody else won is the last time Jitterbug didn't play in it."

"I guess that makes sense," I said. "After all, I understand Jitterbug holds the course record here."

"This ain't the only place. Jitterbug shot the low round at a dozen other courses, too. Not only that, he played in the North Carolina State Open four times, and won all four times. He turned down the prize money, and stayed an amateur. The man could've made a fortune as a professional; still could, but never had any interest. For some reason he hardly plays in any tournaments at all these days; just the club championship here at Muni, which he always wins, and a two-man event he plays with Pinky Paxton every spring. Besides that, he just walks down the fairway like a regular guy, still shootin' lights out. It's the damnedest thing."

"He shot sixty-seven today," I said.

Stan shrugged his shoulders. "That's not even that good for him. Are you gonna play with him again?"

I nodded. "Tomorrow morning."

Stan leaned in as if to share a vital secret. "Everybody knows what you're tryin' to do, Bobby; that you wanna be a professional. And, to be honest, not everybody thinks you can do it." Stan paused, stared into my eyes, and placed the three fingers of his disfigured hand on my forearm. "I suggest you play with Jitterbug every chance you get, and you listen when he speaks. And, I don't mean just his words. You listen to what that man is really saying. Did you hear me, Bobby? You listen to Jitterbug. He's your best chance."

The phone rang. Stan picked it up, and covered the receiver with his hand. "Go on, I already told you what I wanted to say."

And, I walked to the first tee.

An Invitation

Shortly after clocking in, I could see Jessica through the small window in the kitchen door. "You have two tables," she said, smiling. "Three people at sixty-one and a deuce at sixty-two."

Jessica turned to begin the walk back to her post. "I enjoyed meeting your parents," I said.

Jessica stopped and looked back at me. "What?"

"I enjoyed meeting your parents. I hope your dad wasn't put off when I told him I couldn't play golf."

Jessica rushed up close. "Did you really want to play golf with my dad?"

"Sure. And, I will play with him if he ever invites me again."

"I'm so relieved," Jessica said, stacking her pair of hands on her heart. "I thought you were just being polite."

"I *think* I was polite," I said. "But, I really did want to play."

Jessica walked in closer. "Hey, this might sound weird, but would you like to come over to my house some night after work."

That caught me off guard. "Your house? Like your parents' house?"

Jessica laughed. "Yes, but they'll probably be asleep. We both work next Tuesday night. Will Tuesday night work?"

"Yeah, I guess so. I mean, I don't see why not."

Go to her house, watch a movie, get home in time to get some sleep. First tee time every morning. She's beautiful, but I can't miss a chance to play with Jitterbug.

Chapter Five

The golf swing is a dance; you first have to learn the steps, and after that, get with the beat. The trouble is, you can't accomplish the second part as long as the first part still requires thought.
– Jitterbug Bell

Stay Light

"Great touch," Jitterbug said, "is something you can't have without first holding the club lightly. But even then, you have to keep it light throughout the entire swing."

He said too many golfers try to grab the club as it nears impact, as if trying to manage the moment of club and ball contact. "For most folks," he said, "the club stops swinging and starts jabbing just before contact with the ball."

Jitterbug once had me perform what he called a "sense drill" to teach me about grip pressure. This is where I would hit shots focused solely on maintaining a steady, light hold on the club.

"What's the target?"

"There is no target," Jitterbug said. "Just let the ball get in the way of an uninterrupted swinging of the club. The only way you're doing it wrong is if you squeeze the club tighter as you swing."

I remember the first time I tried it. It's hard to explain, but performing the drill made me feel the way Fred Couples looks. The transition from backswing to downswing happened without any manufactured stops or starts. My follow-through felt like a glide to a finish rather than a crash landing. Great weight had been lifted by not having to worry with results, and for the first time, I could actually feel the head of the club *swing*.

Still, I couldn't immediately take it to the course. Concern for accessing the hole kept me from trusting my motion enough to let the club swing without tightening up at impact. But what I could do was *sense* when and where the tightening took place.

"I can feel my hands tighten," I said. "And, I see what you mean; it happens just an instant before impact."

"Feeling it is the first step," Jitterbug said. "And, the second step is to not resist it. Resistance is a form of struggle, and when you struggle you're practicing struggling. To practice struggling is to bring on more of it. Struggle is the opposite of what we want to do. Notice the tension, appreciate it's there, and let it work itself out. Little by little you can soften things up."

In a short time the mid-swing tightening went away. As the tightening went away so did my ball contact improve.

"Mental strain comes as a package deal with muscular tension," Jitterbug said. "So, a case of tight hands is really just a tight brain. There can be no swing, not a *true swing* anyway, where there are tight muscles. And, so you have to spend at least part of the time just working on being relaxed."

Home Work

Jitterbug and I hit our tee shots on the par three eighteenth hole, and picked up our bags to begin the walk down the hill to the final green. "Hey, when we get done here in a minute, I want to show you some of the work I've been doing?"

"What kind of work?"

"I've been writing down golf lessons as they come to me. I guess you could call it my golf journal. Before I go to bed at night I think back on what you and I talked about in our morning round, and get my black notebook out and write. It's a great way to fall asleep. I love to write, always have, so I'm really enjoying it."

"Terrific, Bobby. I can't wait to see what you wrote."

After our round, Jitterbug went to get us each an iced tea, and I, to my truck to retrieve my black spiral bound notebook. I returned to the concession area, flipped my journal open to page one, and placed it on the table in front of Jitterbug. "Tell me what you think."

Journal Entry #1

None-to-none shot: no wrist action on backswing; none on follow through. Wrists only good for power or hitting the ball high. Keep wrists out of shot if possible.

Journal Entry #2

Some-to-none shot: Some wrist action on backswing, none on the way through. Use it whenever I have to stop the ball quickly.

Jitterbug raised his eyebrows before nodding his head. "This is a great start, Bobby. May I make one suggestion?"

Oh great, he doesn't like it. "Sure, of course."

"Well, think about this. There will come a time when you have a whole lot of entries in this journal. And, when that time comes, you'll probably want to show it to other people. So, why not give it some context? I mean, you and I know what the none-to-none shot is, when you're supposed to play it, all that. But, the next person probably won't. You say you enjoy writing; why not write it like you're writing for a golf magazine. It's good either way, but just something for you to consider in case..."

"You're absolutely right. I should write it like I'm handing it into Mrs. Thill in 12th grade writing class. She told me I had a gift for writing. I'll write like I'm handing it in to Mrs. Thill."

"There you go then, Bobby," Jitterbug said. "Write it for Mrs. Thill. I'm sure she'd be happy to know you're using your gift."

Surrender To Gravity

It was a beautiful thing to watch. Each ball seemed to dance after landing, each to the same gentle beat. It didn't appear the ball had even been struck, but rather, cast, still on a string as it came to rest near the hole.

I studied his technique, and noticed his body stayed still; not frozen in place, but centered, and relaxed. His hands were passive, yet athletic and agreeable.

He didn't appear to be staring at any part of the ball prior to impact, and made no effort to keep his head down after. Yet, it was clear he was aware of the ball's location. With obvious comfort, Smiley spun pitch after pitch over the bunker, and did so until there were no more balls at his feet.

"Hey Smiley," I said. "What do you say I pick those balls up for you?"

"Be my guest," he said. "I'm done practicing. Gather 'em up and they yours."

I'd already picked the balls up from around the hole by the time Smiley had himself organized, and was on his way to the parking lot. The thought of pitching the ball from the same place I'd watched Smiley pitch it intrigued me, as I imagined the area around the cup must be pretty soft, and maybe Smiley had found an especially good place from which to spin a short pitch. I poured the small pile out at my feet and hit the first ball several feet past the hole. Soon, I knew where I needed to land the ball for it to roll up close, but found it discouraging I couldn't send it all the way to the hole and stop it like Smiley did. It seemed impossible to create so much spin on such a short shot. I turned around to find Jitterbug watching me from under a shade tree near the small practice area.

"How long have you been watching me?"

"Long enough to know what you're up to."

"How in the heck does Smiley get the ball to spin like he does?"

Jitterbug walked down from beneath the tree. This was sure to be a lesson in philosophy, probably something along the lines of "play your own game and don't worry about what other people do."

"You get backspin from acceleration," Jitterbug said.

"Oh, so I gotta swing harder at the ball?"

"Nah, don't confuse swinging harder with accelerating through impact." I tried to imagine what one must do in order to have the club pick up speed without swinging harder when Jitterbug said, "There's only one way to achieve true and consistent acceleration."

"And how is that?"

"*Gravity*," he said. "You have to be willing to give the club to gravity if you want the club to truly accelerate."

"All right, I'm willing."

"It's not that easy. You can't just decide you're going to do it and think suddenly it's done. It takes a little faith and a little time."

I didn't feel like waiting to acquire either one. Before he could finish his sentence, I gave it another go, but the shot had even less stopping power than before.

"You don't *try* to give the club to gravity," Jitterbug said. "You can only offer it."

Jitterbug reached down to adjust my grip. Holding the shaft of my club with one hand, he rotated my hands counter-clockwise on the grip. With my hands repositioned, he put two fingers on the shaft of my club and began to swing it back and through, creating a slightly longer motion with each pass by the ball.

"That's it," he whispered. "Soft hands. Loosen your arms. Left shoulder back, right hip through. Gravity, Bobby. Surrender to gravity. Gravity knows what to do with it. Left shoulder back, right hip through."

After several passes back and through, I placed my wedge behind a ball. Jitterbug's words echoed as I glided through the motion. *Gravity, Bobby. Loosen your arms. Surrender to gravity. Left shoulder back, right hip through.* The ball left my wedge much softer than before – as if I'd hit no more than a pocket of air – ballooned high and, landed near the flag where it stopped within a foot.

"That felt better," I said. "But, it didn't grab the green and jump back like Smiley's. What'd I do wrong."

Jitterbug shook his head. "You didn't do anything wrong. You're just not there yet. Learning to surrender is the time-line, Bobby; the long, often painful journey from beginner to expert. You can't learn it in a day."

"How long does it take?"

"That depends on you. But believe me, there will come a time when you have the faith to surrender that club. When you do your body will work with gravity and the motion will feel like nothing more than a club attached to a smooth, turning axis, and the grooves on the club will grab the ball and make it dance the way Smiley's balls do."

Not a day on the course goes by I don't think of Smiley hitting those pitch shots. It was, indeed, a beautiful thing to watch.

JOURNAL ENTRY #1 (REVISED)

The Basics Of Wedge Play

When it comes to scoring, there are only two occasions when a golfer can be sure, beyond doubt, a shot has been saved: 1) a shot that goes into the hole, or 2) a shot, hit from off the green, that finishes so close to the hole the following putt cannot be missed.

It is on this latter point I will touch today.

When there is no clear advantage to hitting the ball high, it is best to hit chip shots low to the ground. A shot that stays low is easier to control, as it will take a more predictable first bounce. A ball coming in steep, on the other hand, will often, and sometimes for no apparent reason, bounce left or right; that is to say, act apart from what the golfer had in mind.

The low chip shot can be hit with a sand-wedge, provided the golfer tilts the shaft of the club forward at address. This means the shaft of the club, in the starting position, is leaned left, and the butt end of the grip points more or less at the golfer's left shoulder. From this position, the golfer should perform a none-to-none motion, which is a short swing with no wrist action on the backswing, and no wrist action on the downswing – a wrist-less chipping motion. This none-to-none chipping motion is the foundation upon which a golfer's short game should be built.

"Wow, what a difference!" Jitterbug exclaimed. "You keep it up, Bobby, and before you know it, you'll have a body of work to be proud of."

Reality

Jessica's home was as beautiful on the inside as the outside would lead one to expect. "Kick your shoes off and come on in," she said.

I did as she asked, walked in, and was immediately drawn to photos on the wall by the door. The one that caught my attention was of Jessica on what looked like a gymnastics floor, down on the mat in a full split. She had on a Leotard, and both arms outstretched; one above her head and the other to her side. It was clearly an action shot. "Wow, you're flexible. Can you still do that?"

Jessica laughed. "I sure hope so. That wasn't all that long ago."

"I take it you're a gymnast?"

"Not anymore, but I used to be."

Jessica wore a tee shirt and pajama bottoms, and her hair was still damp from her shower. "That's pretty impressive. What else can you do?"

There was a moment's pause as Jessica tucked in her shirt. "I can do *this*," she said, leaning rearward into a backbend. *So that's why she tucked her shirt in. I guess there will be no free shows.* After a few seconds, she returned forward to a standing position, facing me only a few inches away. Jessica grabbed onto my forearm as if to keep her balance. "Oh goodness, big time head rush," she said. I put my other hand around her waist to help keep her upright. Time stood still as Jessica stared up at me, took in a big breath, exhaled, and shivered. "You just gave me goosebumps."

"I didn't want you to fall."

Jessica's eyes began to taper as she lifted her chin, narrowing the already tiny space between us. *Is this really happening? Just like that? It sure. . . looks that way…*

Our moment was interrupted by the sound of a door opening and the light turning on from the staircase at Jessica's back. "Honey?"

I jumped back, startled. Jessica answered, "Yes, Mom?"

"Do you have company?"

"Yes, Bobby is here."

"Oh, hi Bobby!"

Hearing my name echo from the stairwell caught me off guard. "Uh, hi Mrs. Carrington, or sorry, I mean Margaret."

Margaret laughed. "Goodnight you two."

"Goodnight, Mom."

"Goodnight, Margaret!" I was on sensory overload.

Jessica took me by the hand. "What do you say we move over to the couch? We can put on a movie and get you off your feet." She put in the romantic comedy, *Can't Buy Me Love*, which I'd seen before, but told her I'd watch again.

Jessica started the movie and plopped back down on the couch. "So, where did you go to college?"

"I didn't," I said.

"At all?"

"No, I didn't go at all."

"You're going to be a golf pro and you didn't even play golf in college?"

"No, I didn't," I said. "Is it a big deal?"

Jessica walked over and turned down the volume on the TV, and returned, not to the couch, but to the recliner some six feet away. "It's not a big deal," she said, "but I'm confused. You told me you weren't good at golf. I assumed you were kidding."

"Why would I kid about that?" I said. "I'm still a long way from being good. Like maybe five years. It could be longer than that. I just started playing last summer."

"Last summer? As in one year ago?"

"Yeah, that's right. Why?"

"Did you at least play other sports in high school?"

I didn't particularly care for the trajectory of this conversation. "No, not in high school."

Jessica leaned forward until her feet landed on the floor. "So, let me get this straight. You never played any other sport, and last year, just like that, decided to pick up golf, and..."

"I didn't say I never played any other sport. I said I didn't play any sports *in high school*."

"What does that mean? Were you an athlete in elementary school? A child prodigy who lost his magic touch?"

Jessica smiled playfully, but I wasn't amused. "Maybe so. Should we go over it again? I didn't go to college, wasn't an athlete in high school, and didn't start playing golf until last year. Is there anything else you'd like to know?"

Jessica seemed taken aback. "Did I hit a nerve? I was trying to be funny. We can get off the subject if you want. It's no big deal."

"Yeah, let's get off the subject," I said. "But, before we do, I want you to keep one thing in mind."

"What's that?"

"That I'm gonna do what I say I'm gonna do, Jessica. I'm the first person on the golf course every day, and I stay there right up until I have to be at work. On rainy days, I go to the library and read all the books I can find on the subject of writing. I'm teaching myself to be a writer. I play golf all day, work at night, and write in my journal last thing before I go to bed. I'm going to succeed, Jessica. I'm determined."

Jessica forced a smile. "Then I'm sure you will do fine," she said.

There was no way to deny what we had five minutes ago was gone. Not since the day Carrie announced the end of our relationship, making it final, had I felt as inadequate as I did sitting on that couch watching a movie about a guy dating a girl way out of his league. Less than ten minutes into the film I stood up and turned toward the door. "It's probably time for me to go."

"Okay, no problem. Thanks for coming over."

The Will To Keep Trying

Jitterbug and I waited for the rain to stop, safely inside the shelter house near the fourth tee. "You know, Bobby, I've been meaning to ask you something. There was a young lady at your work you planned to spend an evening with. I believe her name is Jessica. How is that going?"

I hoped the topic of Jessica would simply fade away. "Oh, her? Not much to report. I don't think I want to see her again."

Something in my selection of words got Jitterbug's attention. "So, just to be clear, you're not returning her calls? Is that what you're telling me?"

Must you get to the bottom of it? "No, it's not that," I said. "We're just from two different worlds. I'm busy with golf and she's going back to school soon. It just didn't work out."

Jitterbug seemed to study my expression, and paused before offering his reply. "That's too bad. She sounds like a nice young lady." Jitterbug reached over and pulled the putter from his golf bag. Pretending to change the subject, he said, "Let me ask you something, Bobby. Have you ever set up over a short putt, maybe only three or four feet in length, and for some reason just know you can't make it? I mean, you just know, no matter what, that putt isn't going in the hole. You ever felt that before?"

"Happens all the time," I said. "And I usually prove myself right. It's maddening."

Jitterbug nodded. "It used to be maddening for me, too. But, not any more. The difference now is how I deal with it."

"How's that?"

"Well, it took years, but I figured out the problem is with my head, not my stroke. I finally decided, no matter what, I better not stroke that putt until I get rid of the doubt. That's the first order of business. Get rid of the doubt because doubt leads to fear, and fear takes away a guy's will to keep trying."

Journal Entry #9

The Courage To Continue

Anybody who's played golf, no matter how well or badly, has no doubt fallen witness to the natural ups and downs the game presents. It can be maddening, and difficult to accept, that during one's best stride the edge that appeared so sharp can dull in an instant, and become quite blunt indeed.

Oddly, it's not usually a difficult situation that forms the crack; rather, the cables of concentration are most likely to fail in the face of a seemingly easy, straight-forward task. A simple shot taken for granted, and then missed, can tax a player's spirit so that desire, the most precious of mental commodities, is difficult to maintain.

When pointing to those who have potential, and away from those who don't, a great deal is made of ball striking. It's been said countless times: "Wow, she swings that driver like a tour pro," or, "He shot sixty-five yesterday. That's good enough to win anywhere!"

And, it likely is. But, will that sixty-five still show up after one or two easy putts slide by the hole? Or, will it turn into eighty-two?

To most, eighty-two sounds pretty good, but the question is the same for all, regardless of relative skill. How might we all try our hearts out for every shot that can be saved? Where do we find the courage to work just as hard on the putt for triple bogey as the one for birdie?

It is this quality the great possess, and the should-be-great have yet to acquire. The golfer who, after a miss, can approach the next shot with the same determination as before the flub, is the player to watch.

*****

The rain continued for several days. Jitterbug and I, both carrying umbrellas, teed off on the first hole, where moments later, he gave me the news. "Bobby, I'm afraid I won't be able to play much the next couple of months."

Oh, please don't say that. "Why?"

"My good friend, Pinky Paxton, owns a lawn care business. He has about twenty employees during the summer months, but a bunch of them go back to school this week. So, I usually help him as much as he needs until things slow down in the fall."

"I'm sorry to hear that," I said. "It won't be the same walking this golf course without you."

Jitterbug smiled. "Don't worry, Bobby. I'll still see you around. I help coach the Asheville High School golf team, and we practice here at Muni week days after school. Our first practice is tomorrow."

I tried to find the words to fit. "Well, for what it's worth, I just want you to know I appreciate all the help you've given me, and..."

"No need for all that, Bobby. We're not through. It's just I can't play every day for a while. You keep doing what you're doing, and we'll be back at it in no time."

I'll try to make the most of it.

Chapter Six

You can kick the ball off the tee box,
and still par any hole out there.
But, if you three putt you can't par none of 'em.
– T-Ball Taylor

Lord Berry

Standing on the ninth green within three feet of the hole I had only the simple task of rolling in my short putt to shoot forty-four. This would be my first ever nine-hole score below forty-five, and the beginning, I thought, of a succession of eighteen hole scores under ninety.

I'd narrowly missed a putt of the same length on the previous green, which would've been a two on the par three eighth hole. The thought occurred to me, *What if I were to miss this one, too*? I stabbed at the short putt and knocked the obstinate sphere four feet past the hole. In case that weren't enough I left the come-backer short, too. Tapping in for a double-bogey six, four shots of which were played on the putting surface, I recognized the import of what just occurred. Instead of forty-three, I shot forty-six. To miss a short putt is to throw away a stroke, and I'd cast away three in two holes.

It didn't end there; the back nine greens had their way with me, too. The next morning was worse still. Every new day seemed to follow the same pattern. Early in the round I'd miss a putt of no more than three or four feet in length. The one that followed seemed doubly hard. The fear of finishing a hole made the game seem impossible.

It was hard to ignore the symptoms, as it was clear I had a case of "the yips." *What a time for Jitterbug to take his leave of absence. Surely he could help me.* My troubles started less than a week after our last round together and quickly progressed to full death spiral mode, still not three weeks into it.

There was plenty of free advice available, as everybody had a solution. I'd given most of it at least half a try. But nothing made sense. Nothing, that is, until the day I shared the practice green with a retired Englishman named Clayton "Lord" Berry.

Lord Berry was a twenty-year resident of the Blue Ridge Mountains, but his lack of Southern hospitality made it clear he was from some other part of the world. Lord Berry seemed to take delight in other people's struggles and loved nothing more than the opportunity to publicly undress one's morale.

Lord Berry wasn't a teaching professional by trade or affiliation, but that didn't stop him from offering advice to anyone whose method he thought needed his help. Tall and lanky with a pointed chin and a huge Adam's apple, Lord Berry walked slowly, and slower yet, it seemed, if he was in front of me when I was in a hurry.

Although just an ordinary ball striker, Lord Berry twice took Jitterbug to extra holes in the club championship. Most locals considered him the best putter in western North Carolina.

"What are you trying to do?" Lord Berry asked me in his trademarked, scornful tone.

"I'm trying to make some putts," I said.

"You're not trying to "make" anything. You're trying desperately not to miss."

Lord Berry was the last guy I'd ever look to for advice. I avoided making eye contact, hoping he'd get the hint and leave me alone. "I'm sorry, Bobby, I didn't hear you," he said. "Perhaps you wouldn't mind repeating yourself."

"You didn't hear me because I didn't say anything. Look, you practice your way and I'll practice mine." I kept my head down, hoping the interrogation would cease.

"Let me guess. You're keeping your head down. You're keeping your weight on your forward foot. You're making sure your arms hang naturally so your putter is soled squarely on the green. I suspect you've also thrown into this putting *stew* of yours some thoughts of taking the putter back with a minimal amount of wrist-hinging with hopeful intentions of returning through in the same manner. Did I leave anything out?"

I hated he could see through me. Embarrassed, I said, "No, I think that's about it."

"Oh, I disagree," he said. "Something very important has been left out."

"Oh yeah? And, what's that?"

"The hole! You've forgotten about the hole."

Ridiculous. I haven't forgotten about the hole. "My problem doesn't have anything to do with the hole. I've just gotta practice until I get my touch back."

"Uh-huh, nothing to do with the hole. You're just looking to regain some lost 'touch,' is that it?"

"Okay, Mr. Berry, what's your point?"

"The point is that even the best putters miss more putts than they make. But you can't accept that. And when you miss you immediately look for a mechanical flaw to blame. You might find you have plenty of touch if you spent more time thinking about the hole and less time thinking about your stroke. You are so consumed with *not missing* you've lost sight of what a good attempt is. To you, a putt that goes in can only be ascribed to luck, and the one you miss is further evidence your stroke is flawed. I suspect you hate putting."

Maybe I did hate putting but I'd had enough. I looked at my watch. "Oh my gosh!" I said. "Is that the time? Looks like this lesson is over. I'd like to stick around but I won't. Thank you. Good-bye."

I went in the clubhouse and sat down until Lord Berry went off the first tee. When I went back out, I happened upon Jitterbug, who stood next to the putting green with the Asheville High School golf team. Just as I was about to say hello, Jitterbug motioned for me to look at the kids from his high school team rolling putts on the green. There were five players, all set up at eight feet from their respective holes. One after the other they rolled their eight footers at the cup.

The team members all fist pumped, celebrating the putts that dropped. Just as notable to me, however, was the thrill they got from the ones that narrowly missed. It was as if the whole thing was a lark. *Mission accomplished when the ball goes in, good try when it doesn't.* Given my own troubles I wasn't all that happy for them.

"Jitterbug, you should have heard what Lord Berry tried to tell me about..."

"Man these kids can really putt!" Jitterbug said. "You know why kids are such good putters?"

"No."

"Look at them. See how they look at the hole? They can't take their eyes off of it. They act like they might sneak up on it or something."

I took a closer look. The kids seemed entranced by the hole, taking the putter back only after the right amount of focus had been met.

"The problem with most adults is they don't think about the

hole. They're too busy thinking about all the stuff they've heard they're supposed to do. 'Set your feet like this, position your eyes like that,' I'm sure you've heard all that stuff, Bobby."

I certainly had. "Yes sir, Bobby, good putters are thinking about the hole. Bad putters are thinking about the way they're supposed to stroke it."

There was a moment's pause. "I'm sorry," Jitterbug said. "I interrupted you. What was that about Mr. Berry?"

A little ashamed of how I'd acted, I said, "Ahh, nothing."

"Well, if Mr. Berry was trying to teach you about putting I suggest you take some time out and listen."

The experience left me wondering how many precious gems of advice I had missed out on in my life because I didn't care for the messenger.

That marked the beginning of the end of my putting struggles.

The Free-Throw

Lord Berry spent hours putting the same four-footer. He'd often be on the putting green when I teed off, still there at the turn, and stay there long after I finished my round.

The day Jitterbug returned from his lawn mowing hiatus, the two of us walked by the putting green on the way to the back nine. "You know, if Lord Berry has so much time to practice, it seems to me he should divide his time between short, medium, and long distance putts, not just four-footers."

Jitterbug's face lit up as he put his bag down near the tenth tee. Smiling, he said, "Did I ever tell you about playin' basketball with my cousin, Hardpan, when we were kids?"

"Not that I can recall."

"Hardpan didn't care a thing about dribbling the ball, but he could shoot! He used to go down to the park and spend all day on the free-throw line. All day long. He could make a hundred in a row. And, not just from the free-throw line; he could shoot it from anywhere. If we were playing a game, I knew all I had to do was find Hardpan open, and it was two points. A guaranteed two points!"

"He could really shoot it, huh?"

"That's right," Jitterbug said. "He only practiced free-throws, but he could shoot it from anywhere; a lay-up or twenty-five feet; open on the floor, or four guys with their hands in his face, it didn't matter. His stroke was so pure, and the ball felt so good in his hands, he could just fire at it. You knew he'd make it. And, a game of H-O-R-S-E?!? He was unbeatable. I'm talking UN-beatable!"

Jitterbug, returning to the here and now, said softly, "Hmm. And, you know, it's funny. I asked Hardpan one day why it was he just practiced free-throws. He looked at me and said, 'Jitterbug, most people practice missing, but I practice making. And, that's why I can make it from anywhere. I practice making.'"

"So, are you saying Lord Berry putting four-footers is like Hardpan shooting free-throws? He's practicing making?"

Jitterbug shook his head. "I'm not saying anything. But, I can tell you one thing for sure. Mr. Berry is the best putter I've ever seen, and I'm not about to question the way he spends his practice time."

Journal Entry #22

Firm Or Die

There are many who, when discussing the correct pace of a putt, like to say, "Never up, never in." And, while this ordinary truth is, to many, a great truth, it shows no deeper insight than the observation that a ball putted past the cup didn't drop in either. Forgotten, too, is the farther past the hole a putt rolls, the more certain it never had a chance.

Too often, I've heard a well-wishing fellow player instruct, "Okay partner, no matter what, at least get it to the hole." What follows is usually pitiful at best. Instead of focusing on what's required to hole the putt, the advice taker is now consumed with not committing the cardinal sin of leaving an important putt short. The consciousness is of not doing rather than doing, a thundercloud in the mind of the golfer.

Thus, it is unwise to adhere to a blanket firmness philosophy, as this is time spent away from dealing with the task at hand, which is imagining the ball going into the hole.

Chapter Seven

Why would I go to the lake?
If it's nice enough to be on the water
it's nice enough to play golf.
– T-Ball Taylor

A Surprise Visit

December of 1993 was the coldest final month of the year in nearly four decades, a fact I considered inconvenient. On my way into Vincenzo's, three days before Christmas, I kicked the snow from my black dress shoes and shuffled in the front door. There were opening waiter duties to perform, the extent of which I couldn't be sure about until I made the trip upstairs to check out the condition of the tables. One's eyes need only reach the level of the top stair to see straight into the second floor dining room. My heart dropped when I discovered Jessica sitting all alone at table twelve.

"You're the last person I expected to see here."

Jessica stood up, slowly walked over, and reached out to give me a hug. "Merry Christmas," she said, only slightly louder than a whisper.

"Merry Christmas, how have you been?"

Jessica loosened her hold, took a step back, and dropped her gaze. "I'm fine. Listen, I know you have work to do, and I won't keep you. I just need to tell you something, and then I'll go."

"What's that?"

"I don't know what happened at my house that night. I wish I could go back and figure out what I said because all at once things changed and they never changed back. I wanted to ask before I left for school but you didn't even stick around to say good-bye on my last night. Anyway, I'm sorry for what I said."

"I appreciate you stopping by, Jessica. You're right, I have to get this dining room ready to go."

Jessica looked up, visibly irritated. "What is wrong with you? I took a big chance walking in here today. Either tell me you don't like me, or tell me what I did, or tell me to leave you alone, but tell me *something*."

"Okay, I'll tell you," I said. "I started playing golf at twenty years old, which means I don't have time to stop and stutter every time somebody questions my ambition, or motivation, or whatever. You want a guy who's in college, and that takes me out of the race."

Jessica shook her head. "No, that's not what I want," she said. "I mean, I do want that, but not because it means so much to me. It's my dad. He considers college the very least a person should be able to do. If I seemed bothered at my house that night, it's because I was trying to think of what my dad would say. He knows how much I like you, but if he found out you were putting off school until after you got good at golf; then to find out you just started playing golf. . . I don't know what he would say."

"Jessica, I'm sorry, but can we talk about this some other time?"

Jessica softened her expression. "When?"

"Any time other than now," I said. "I have to get this room ready."

She wasn't about to let me off the hook. "Tomorrow night then. Jay asked me to hostess a few nights while I'm on break from school.

I wanted to wait until I saw you before I told him yes or no. I'll tell him yes."

"Sure, tell him yes," I said. "That's fine."

"Okay. We'll talk tomorrow then."

At that, Jessica walked down the stairs, and out into the cold.

*****

Christmas break, the time during which Jessica was home from school, came and went without us having the talk she requested; and to which I agreed. I couldn't stand the thought of where a discussion like that might lead.

She might ask me about my last relationship, and why Carrie found it so easy to let me go. I might have to answer questions about whether or not I've ever been in trouble, or if my parents are still together. Why go through all of that when, in the end, her father won't approve of me? It seems easier to just try to forget about her.

The Power Of Commitment

Finishing our first round of 1994, I thought about life, and how eighteen months had passed since my lonely drive from Indiana to North Carolina.

As we often did, Jitterbug and I followed our round with an iced tea and a scorecard review.

"Can I ask your opinion on something?"

Jitterbug glanced up from the scorecard. "You shot eighty-eight today," he said. "Not your best, but not bad in forty-degree weather."

"I'll take it," I said.

Jitterbug put the scorecard down, and removed his glasses. "I'm sorry, did you say you wanted my opinion on something?"

I nodded. "Yes. This isn't really about golf. It's about this girl. You may remember I talked about her last summer."

"Of course," Jitterbug said. "Her name is Jessica."

"That's the one," I said. "But, let's back up a little. I didn't play any sports in high school, didn't go to college, none of that. Now, I'm telling everybody I'm going to be a golf professional, and I'm not even good at golf. My own mother, who's as sweet as can be, thinks I'm delusional."

"That's great!" Jitterbug exclaimed. "You found your passion!"

Is that what you just heard me say? "That's not really my point," I said. "You see, Jessica's father is a doctor, and apparently he won't like that I never went to college..." Hearing myself speak, I paused, stricken with the same insecurity I'd felt in the days leading up to Carrie leaving for school.

Jitterbug peered at me from across the table. Leaning in, he asked, "Do you have a goal?"

"Yes, I do."

"Are you committed to that goal?"

"Yes, I am."

"Is it a worthwhile goal?"

"Worthwhile? Yes, it is to me."

"That's the answer right there, Bobby," Jitterbug said. "You're not a success when you finally accomplish your goal. You're a success as soon as you commit to it. If you do that you're the equal of anybody else who ever had a goal."

I found Jitterbug's words uplifting, but short of a solution. "Okay, but what do I tell Jessica in the meantime? And, her father?"

"The truth," Jitterbug said, as if it couldn't be simpler. "If asked, just tell the truth."

"Oh, so just say, 'Don't let the fact I'm not good at golf fool you, but you wait and see, I'm gonna be a pro one day.' Is that what I say?"

Jitterbug laughed. "Don't you see, Bobby? You started with nothing. Reaching your goal will be extra satisfying for you. But, until then, don't worry so much about what to tell people because right now they have no reason to believe in you."

"What do you mean?"

"I mean people will judge you based on what you've already done. And, to some people, all you've done is skip out on college. But, you have the power of commitment. You are what you're committed to, not what other people think about you. Just keep living the life of a man workin' on his goal, and the rest of the world will find out when the time comes."

Journal Entry #36

The Rehearsal Swing

The practice swing might well be considered a final chance to gather some short term muscle memory before having to deliver the real thing. With this in mind, the golfer who has a known tendency to swing too fast will likely benefit from performing a rehearsal swing at a slower, controlled pace. The golfer who has a bad habit of finishing on the rear foot should make a decided effort to get to the forward foot during the practice swing – and perhaps even stay there for a beat or two longer than usual.

Whatever the problem area may be, a good practice swing is a well-made beginning. It not only frees the mind for the shot at hand, but does so as easily on the first hole as any of the seventeen that follow.

Chapter Eight

The golf swing starts in the middle of the body,
and works out to the extremities.
Bad golfers swing with just their extremities.
– Mr. Vaughn

Obie Vaughn

The first few months of 1994 brought about a number of hardships, or as Jitterbug called them, "opportunities."

Take, for example, my golf game. One moment, it seemed, I looked forward to leaving in awe the small galleries of older members who collected to watch me tee off. The next moment I wanted to give up the game completely for having lost all my power off the tee.

It wasn't quite as noticeable with a wedge or nine-iron in my hand, but playing any par four over 400 yards in length meant I'd use driver and three-wood, both with as much force as I could muster. The days of getting to those same holes with as little as a sand-wedge for my second shot seemed long gone, and their memory, a mere figment of my imagination.

Everything about my ball flight was weak. My shots just flew high and turned right. Some holes didn't offer enough room down the left side for me to get a shot to stay in the fairway. And, if faced with a left to right wind, forget it, I didn't dare swing the driver.

Despite it all, there was one silver lining; my short game greatly improved. I figured it was just some universal law of accommodation like the blind man who develops extra keen hearing.

Obie Vaughn disagreed. He said the grip I used, more specifically the position of my left hand on the club, was great for chipping and pitching but couldn't be worse for producing yards off the tee.

Mr. Vaughn was Jitterbug's teacher. He had used a wheel chair since returning from Normandy, marred with shrapnel, in 1944. Jitterbug said Mr. Vaughn knew more about the golf swing than "any man alive." Despite his reputation as a legendary teacher, he seldom gave advice, as he was selective when it came to those with whom he'd discuss the inner workings of the golf swing. I wasn't sure he even knew my name until the day he called it out as I prepared to tee off on the first hole. "Hey Bobby! You still hittin' 'em soff?"

Apparently all the times I followed my weak tee shots with excuses like, "Daggone it! I hit it on the heel," or, "I didn't quite catch that one solid" didn't fool him.

A little unnerved I answered, "Yeah, but I think I've got it figured out now."

"Oh, yeah? Let me see ya practice swing."

I gripped the club, ready to take it back when Mr. Vaughn shouted, "Hell no, you ain't figured nothin' out. You want some help or not?" I did want help, but Jitterbug and I were about to play. Before I could answer, Jitterbug said, "You better go, Bobby."

I followed Mr. Vaughn as he wheeled himself to an open area of grass near the ninth green. "Take a grip on that club," he said. I gripped it the way it felt comfortable in my hands.

"See there, you just like the rest of them short hitters. You think the back of your left hand is supposed to face the target.

Look right there, I can see the whole butt end of the club between your two arms."

"Where are you supposed to see the butt end of my club?"

Mr. Vaughn looked at me face-on from his wheel chair some five feet away. "I shouldn't be able to see it at all, not if you got a good grip. Ya left hand should be in the way so the butt end isn't visible. And, when you look down, you shouldn't be able to see any of the ring finger of ya left hand. You gotta hold the club in the fingers of ya left hand, not in ya palm. If you do it right, someone lookin' at ya straight on can't see the butt end of the grip."

I tried holding it the way he suggested and took a practice swing. It felt horrible. Not only was it uncomfortable, it felt like I'd lost control of the clubface. "Hey, you ain't done," he said. "By holding the club wrong all this time, you've trained your hands to work the wrong way. Now you gotta have a wrist-cock and release to match your grip."

I'd heard Jitterbug refer to "the release," but never really knew what it meant. "This time," Mr. Vaughn said, "when you get to the top of the backswing, make sure the club is pressing into ya left thumb print. That's the left hand. On the other hand you should feel the club weighin' down on the base of ya right index finger."

I took three or four practice backswings, each time careful to sense the weight of the club bearing down on the thumb print of my left hand and base of my right index finger. One final time I took the club to the top, held my backswing position, and ask Mr. Vaughn for his nod of approval. "Like this?"

"Looks good at the top," Mr. Vaughn said. "But, you gotta release that club. This time, as you're swinging down through the hitting area allow your right arm to roll over like you're shakin' hands with the target."

I teed a ball and used an eight-iron to quickly hit a shot down the ninth fairway.

WHACK! The ball shot off the face, and curved beautifully to the left. It was by far the most solid strike I'd put on a ball in what seemed like ages. I stood there savoring the moment, having just felt pure, square-faced energy leave my club and go into the ball when Mr. Vaughn announced a quick end to our lesson on the grip. "Whada ya say we get back to the tee?"

I walked alongside Mr. Vaughn on our way back to where we started, and wondered to myself how this grip problem could've happened. "Mr. Vaughn, I used to hit the ball hard with a draw all the time, just like that eight-iron back there. I don't remember ever purposely changing my grip. How did this happen?"

"This is why a guy has to know what he's doing!" Mr. Vaughn exclaimed. "You can play good for short little spells without having any idea of what makes up a good golf swing. But to BE good, you have to fix yourself on the spot. Little things can creep in without you knowing where they came from, and you gotta know what's okay to fiddle with and what's best left alone. It could've been ya looked at some other guy's grip that was different than yours and without thinking much of it moved ya hands a little bit to look like his. Then a little bit turned into a little more, and you unlearned how to release the club. Ya aim got jacked up for having to start ya slice down the left side; ya swing got grooved out-to-in, which as bad as that sounds is the only swing path that'll work with all the other stuff ya had goin' on. And, all this because ya don't know how to fix ya own self when things start to slip a little."

Before I knew it we were back at the first tee. "Mr. Vaughn, I need to pay you for this lesson."

"Oh, you sure gonna," he said. "In the meantime, I don't wanna have to give a golf lesson to everyone you impress with this new, powerful swing. That new grip came to you in a dream. You got that?"

"Yes, sir. Thank you, Mr. Vaughn."

Mr. Vaughn shushed me with his eyes. "Don't thank me! Just go practice releasin' that club until your hands bleed. I'll take another look at ya tomorrow. Now go on."

I thought back on the number of rounds I'd played with that awful slice spin, and wondered why Jitterbug hadn't offered up any help. *We play together five days every week; we hit hundreds of balls on the range; he's witnessed my weak, left-to-right shot more times than I care to recall. Why didn't he say anything about my grip?*

Looking back, I'm glad I didn't ask that question. The fact is I never asked Jitterbug for help. I just complained. Worse yet, I put on the same act for him I tried to put on for Mr. Vaughn, pretending each day I showed up I finally had it figured out.

Jitterbug once said, "A teacher can only teach up to the level of the student's willingness to be taught." I just didn't know he was talking about me.

Journal Entry #49

A Soft Grip

In a proper grip, the club is held primarily in the fingers of the glove hand. Holding it this way, the golfer can grip lightly while still maintaining a sense of security, and be sure it won't be lost during the swing.

Many golfers, because they don't know, or have not yet been convinced, hold the club in the palm of the glove hand. As soon as the swing gets under way, a club held in the palm will begin to shift, creating the need to hold on tighter. Evidence of this can be found in just a quick glance at the golfer's glove. If after one round of golf the glove is starting to show signs of wear in the palm, the glove's owner could benefit from a better understanding of how to hold the club properly.

Dollar Sinks

Jitterbug and I often played a game on the practice green called "dollar sinks." The game goes like this. Whoever has the honor, let's say it's Jitterbug, he putts from wherever he wants. If he makes it, I have to putt from the same spot, and if I miss I owe a dollar. If I make on top of his make he owes me two dollars. It's a great game because it encourages the person with the honor to choose either a long putt, or if not that, something with some pronounced break. To make on top of the other guy's make is the ultimate gut shot in dollar sinks.

One afternoon, already three dollars ahead, and hoping to make it four, I asked, Jitterbug, "Why didn't you ever go out on tour, you know, play golf for a living? The thought must've crossed your mind."

Jitterbug stroked his long putt, hoping to cap the one I just made, but left it short. "One thing I've learned, and you will too, is you can do anything you want to in this world."

"I believe that," I said.

"You can do anything you want, but you can't do *everything* you want. You have to make choices. You have to decide what's worth your commitment, and to me it wasn't golf."

"What got in your way?"

"Nothing got in my way. Delores and I got married when we were both nineteen, and I wanted to be the best husband I could be. For that to happen I always felt like I needed to be there when she got home from work. And, for thirty-two years I've been there. I felt like I needed to sleep in our bed every night, so for thirty-two years I have. I've always wanted Delores to know she's the most important thing in my life, so I don't talk about golf when I'm with her. If I played professionally I'd have to talk about the game all the time. And, I'd have to leave for weeks on end. So I chose a good marriage over a career as a golfer; in my mind there is no way I could have both. I've never once regretted my decision."

Jitterbug cut grass for thirty years, and never once regretted choosing that over being a superstar in the world of golf. That's unimaginable to me. I bet if somebody asked Delores, she'd tell them she has a good husband.

Chapter Nine

Without the right fundamentals, your good shots are always gonna be less frequent. You gonna be stuck in that 7-, 8-, 9-handicap range forever.
– Jitterbug Bell

The Kids' Clinic

Jitterbug didn't usually play golf on the weekends, but he'd sometimes go with me to The Practice Tee, the range down the street from Muni. We might be there for two hours and not go through more than a hundred balls between us. We'd spend most of our time just listening to what was going on around us. Jitterbug took particular delight in watching the teaching pros give lessons.

Every pro within fifty miles knew Jitterbug and it was interesting to watch them teach, knowing full well they were in the presence of a local legend. Some seemed to rise to the occasion, some tried too hard. There was one occasion, however, when a local pro did *not* try too hard. In fact, he didn't even show up.

"Someone better tell me I didn't bring my kids out here for nothin'!" came a sudden shout.

It was time for the Saturday morning kids' clinic, only the second of the season, and the instructor, Alan Baker, was nowhere to be found.

Fighting back a grin, I said, "I'd hate to be Alan come next week. He's gonna get an earful."

Jitterbug stood solemnly as he removed the head cover from his driver. "He'll be lucky to have a next week."

Alan Baker was well known for his success on the Mountain Tour. Unfortunately, he was just as well known for not being on time to teach his golf lessons.

Walking to the edge of the tee, Jitterbug let out a whistle. "All right, kids, let's have everybody in the clinic grab a seven-iron out of your bag and put your bag against the wall. When you've done that, come on over, circle around and have a seat."

This would be worth watching. Jitterbug and I weren't there the week before, so there was no way for him to know where they'd left off, or if his help would even be welcome.

Mr. Deck, the driving range owner, stepped out of the work shack with a cordless phone pressed to his ear. With angry mothers swarming all around, he looked out to the tee, and dropped the phone down to his side. "Ladies, I apologize for the confusion," he said. "But, Mr. Baker won't be with us anymore. The good news, however, is that Harold Bell will teach today's clinic."

Unimpressed by the sudden change, one mother barked, "We paid for Alan Baker, not Harold Bell!"

Mr. Deck smiled. "I'll make a deal with you, Mrs. Thompson. Just stay for one lesson. If you're unsatisfied with Jitterbug Bell, your child can hit balls all summer for free."

Seemingly awe struck, Mrs. Thompson looked out to the tee. "You mean to tell me that man is Jitterbug Bell?"

Jitterbug put a ball on a tee and hit a drive as long and straight as I'd ever seen. When it came to rest close to the end of the range Jitterbug turned and asked the kids, "What did I do to that ball?"

One of the younger kids yelled out, "You killed it!!"

There was a small roar as Jitterbug nodded and agreed. "That's right, I killed it! Anybody want to know how to kill the ball?"

"Yeah!! Kill the ball!!" the kids cheered loudly, and began to stand up.

"Now, hang on a minute," Jitterbug said. "Stay seated for just another minute and listen to me. You kids gotta do exactly as I say if you're gonna learn how to kill the ball. Everybody has to agree to listen, 'cause you can't just hear a little bit, you gotta hear the whole thing or you won't be able to kill the ball. Now, raise your hand if you agree to listen." About half of the kids raised their hands.

"That's too bad," Jitterbug said. "If all of you don't agree then we can't even get started."

A teenage boy with his hand in the air turned to the rest of the group, ordering, "Raise your hand you guys! Raise your hands or he's not going to teach us!"

WHHAAACCKK!!!! Jitterbug drove another ball down the range. At that, arms shot up across the tee.

"Good. Now, the first lesson in killing the ball is getting into a *K-stance.* K stands for kill the ball. And that's what we plan to do, right?"

"Yeaahh!!!" the kids shouted out. "Kill it!!!"

Jitterbug addressed the ball with his chin buried in his chest, his shoulders rounded, his hips pushed forward, and his knees severely bent.

"Does this look like a K-stance?" It was clear Jitterbug wasn't in the same position he'd been in when he hit the long drives. "NO!!!" the kids said, shaking their heads.

"That's right! This looks more like an S-stance, doesn't it?"

The kids seemed to identify the S formed by Jitterbug's posture. "And what does S stand for?" Jitterbug asked.

One child yelled out, "Sloppy!"

Apparently caught off guard, Jitterbug laughed. "That's right! Sloppy! What else does S stand for?"

"Silly!" another child giggled.

"Good. What else?" When no child replied, Jitterbug said, "How about soft?"

Again, a roar from the kids, "SOFT!!!!"

"Short?"

"Yeah, Short!!!!"

"Sorry?"

"Sorry!!!"

"How about slice?"

"Yeah!!!!"

"Now, you better believe," Jitterbug said, "if you stand like an S, you're gonna hit the sloppiest, softest, shortest, silliest, and sorriest slices you've ever seen!"

With the parents all smiling in appreciation for this most unexpected show, Jitterbug hit a shot from the S-stance, sending the ball, along with a chunk of ground, weakly to the right. The kids roared with laughter.

"So, I don't want to see any S-stances," Jitterbug said. "Everybody understand that?" The kids nodded.

Jitterbug addressed a ball with no tilt anywhere in his posture. His legs were straight, and so was his torso. "Now, what does this stance look like?" he asked. When nobody answered, Jitterbug said, "Looks like an I, doesn't it?"

"Yeah, I!!!"

"And, what does I stand for?

After a few seconds of silence, one child braved softly, "I don't know."

"That's right!" Jitterbug exclaimed. "It could stand for *I don't know*, 'cause anyone who stands this way doesn't know anything about killing the ball! What else does I stand for?"

We heard words like *impossible, ignorant, iffy*, and *in the trees.*

"Then, should I stand like an *I* if I want to kill the ball?"

"NO!!!!"

Jitterbug assumed a proper, more athletic posture and launched a range ball over the 250-yard banner.

"That was a K-stance!" Mrs. Thompson yelled out, then covered her mouth to make her sudden blurt appear accidental. Her teenage son shook his head before covering his face with his hand.

"That's right," Jitterbug said. "Now somebody talk to me about this K-stance. Are my legs severely bent, or just a little bent?"

"Just a little bent!"

"That's right. Are my hands hanging straight down under my chin or are they way out in front of me, stiff like a couple of boards?"

"Hanging straight down under your chin!"

"Am I bending at the waist or tilting from the hips?"

That confused the kids; they all looked at one another for the answer.

Jitterbug hunched over, creating a big bow in his spine. "Well, this would be bending from the waist."

As if to beat the buzzer, one child yelled out, "You're tilting from the hips!"

"That's right," Jitterbug said. "So, my back has to be straight then, right?"

The kids agreed.

"All right, then. If you think you know how to get in a K-stance, you can all get up and show me."

Jitterbug motioned for me to assist. As the kids circled around him, all working into a K-stance, Jitterbug said to me, "They probably worked on their grip last week, but let's go around and make sure they got it right."

When the kids were all armed with a workable grip and stance, they spent the rest of the hour hitting balls down the range.

At the end of the clinic, Mr. Deck approached Jitterbug. "I would love it, and so would the parents, Jitterbug, if you could teach the remaining six weeks of the spring/summer session. You just name your price."

Jitterbug shook his head. "I'm afraid teaching for money would mean I'm no longer an amateur," he said. "That's not something I'm willing to do."

Mr. Deck seemed at a loss for words.

"I'll tell you what, though," Jitterbug said. "You custom fit clubs for people, don't you?"

"I sure do," Mr. Deck said. "You want me to make you a new set of clubs?"

"Not for me. For the kids. About half of them don't have clubs anywhere near the right size. Why don't you measure them all and make whatever adjustments necessary so they all have the right sized equipment?"

"Done!" Mr. Deck said, nodding. "Anything else?"

Jitterbug turned to face me. "Just one thing. These kids are a lot to handle, Bobby. You think you can give up every Saturday morning to help me teach?"

I couldn't get the words out fast enough. "I'd love to."

Jitterbug turned back to Mr. Deck, and extended his hand. "Then I think we have a deal," he said.

I thought back on Jitterbug's presentation; how he, without time to prepare, managed to bring laughter and excitement to the topic of golf posture, and wondered if I'd be able to perform like that. My best chance, I figured, was to watch Jitterbug.

JOURNAL ENTRY #60

Proper Alignment

Golf presents a particularly unique challenge in that it requires hitting to a memory. Instead of looking at the target during the shot, the golfer's eye must gaze back to the ball before making the swing, as it's necessary to look at the thing one intends to strike. Thus, the target is nowhere in the golfer's view at the moment of impact with the ball.

This makes good aim essential and something that must be established and attended to on a near-constant basis.

Therefore, it is advisable to always use an alignment aid (a club resting on the ground, pointed in the direction of the hole, will do nicely) during each visit to the driving range. It should line up parallel to the intended line of flight. After that, one need only align one's feet parallel to the alignment aid, and soon following, a good sense of proper aim will develop.

Having lined up in a way one can be sure is square, gone is the urge to re-direct the club during the swing. If the golfer practices as I've described, a good sense of proper alignment will not be long in coming.

Summer Break

Jessica finally returned home for summer break. I was beyond delighted to learn she'd be back at the restaurant, attending the hostess stand, and making work something to look forward to.

Arriving at the restaurant, I pulled open the big front door, and discovered Jessica on the other side with a spray bottle and towel. She stood up, put her arms around me, and gave me a double air kiss, European style. "Can you come over to my house next Sunday night for dinner?"

"You mean like dinner with your parents?"

She laughed. "Yes, with my parents. And, with me, too, if that's okay."

It's now or never. "Of course," I said. "That would be very nice."

"Are you sure? Your face tells a different story."

I stood up straight, changed my expression, and did my best to exude genuine honesty. "Jessica, it will be my great pleasure to have dinner with your parents."

The In-Motion Musts

I already played twenty-seven holes, and yet it still wasn't noon. There were a couple of choices with regard to how I might round out the afternoon. I could walk another nine, and still get home in time to take a shower before work. Or, I could get out of the sun, and go visit Mr. Vaughn in the shade near the first tee.

I decided on the latter. After all, I had a few questions for Mr. Vaughn, and it wasn't always easy to find him sitting alone.

Leaning my bag against the big oak tree, I took a seat on the wooden bench next to Jitterbug's life long teacher. "You know, Mr. Vaughn, I realize the basics start with grip, posture, ball position, and alignment, but it seems to me that a time would come when a person is pretty solid in all those areas, so what's next?"

Mr. Vaughn shook his head. "What was that?"

"What was what?"

"Your manners!" Mr. Vaughn exclaimed. "You better speak to me before you just start askin' questions!"

"Oh, I'm sorry," I said. "Let me start over. Hello, Mr. Vaughn. How are you?"

"I'm doing well, and hope you are."

"I'm doing very well, thank you."

"I'm glad to hear that," Mr. Vaughn said. "Next is the in-motion musts."

This is the first I've heard of any musts. "What are the 'in-motion musts?'"

"It's four things you gotta do to hit the ball with any consistent distance and direction. Two of 'em are before impact and two of 'em after. They're the same today as they was a hundred years ago."

I knew better than to rush Mr. Vaughn, but also knew a gentle nudge is sometimes required. "So, are they a secret?"

It took a moment, but Mr. Vaughn finally turned his head to answer. "They are turn, transfer, release, and finish."

TURN:

Mr. Vaughn said the first must is a full turn away from the ball. "The reason people try to swing at the ball so hard is because they don't turn far enough during their back swing. They sense they didn't get fully loaded and try to make up the difference by swinging wildly at the ball."

He went on to say it doesn't matter whether the club gets to parallel or not, as long as the left shoulder turns behind the ball during the backswing.

TRANSFER:

"After that is the weight transfer. Everybody always wants to know what the first move that starts the downswing is. 'Is it the right elbow goin' here?' Or, 'Is it the left knee movin' over there?' It ain't none of that! It's just a weight transfer to the left leg. Same in hitting a golf ball as it is throwing a baseball. You load the front leg, then you turn and swing the body. The weight goes to the forward leg while your back is still to the target."

RELEASE:

"After you've turned and transferred you gotta make sure you release. This is where people fall asleep 'cause nobody pays attention to what they do after impact. But remember, releasin' that clubhead occurs after the ball is already gone."

I thought back on the grip lesson I'd had with Mr. Vaughn; the time he had me hit an eight-iron off of a tee near the ninth green. As I could clearly recall, he instructed me to roll over my forearms through impact. "I remember the release," I said. "You do it with the forearms."

"You're close, but there's more to it than that," Mr. Vaughn said. "You get the idea by doing it with your arms, but it's just a necessary first step. The day the switch flips is the day you take it outta ya arms and put it into your body. Beginner releasers learn to do it with their forearms, and expert players, like Jitterbug, do it with their bodies."

FINISH:

I tried to recite the four in-motion musts so I could remember the last one. "Okay, Mr. Vaughn, there's turn, transfer, and release, and uh, what's the last one again?"

"Finish," Mr. Vaughn replied. "But, keep in mind the finish changes as you get older. See, you young folks is gonna finish with your chest facing *left* of the target. That means the closest thing to the target at your finish should be your right shoulder. But, the older guys, them Senior Tour players you see on Sunday afternoon, they don't finish like that. They used to, but now they finish with their *chest facing* the target. But, to make up for not turnin' as far, they lean a little more toward the target at their finish. Or, at least, that's been my observation."

As important as the in-motion musts are, Mr. Vaughn insisted, they're of no use without first having a good grip, posture, ball position, and alignment.

JOURNAL ENTRY #68

Range Brilliance

Golfers of every level have experienced driving range brilliance, followed by golf course collapse.

There's only one cure for it: play more and practice less. After all, there are many people who never practice, play all the time, and maintain a scratch handicap.

How? While these players may or may not possess technical

excellence, they're familiar with their shot patterns, are accustomed to the "everything counts" mindset the golf course demands, and don't have excess swing thoughts.

On the flip side, range rats too often have no familiarity with their shot patterns (they're ever changing), are bothered by the every-shot-counts prospect of playing the game, and have as many swing thoughts as recent trips to the range.

If practice, rather than play, is the only forum time and money allow, short game work should receive priority. Not only does short-game practice summon fewer technical and mechanical thoughts (short game mechanics are simpler, and the required physical effort, considerably less), it takes pressure off the long game. And, after all, it is pressure that causes problems to begin with.

The Stopwatch

Lord Berry and I had worked out most of our differences, but that doesn't mean I always enjoyed playing golf with him. He simply drove me crazy with all his unsolicited advice on putting. Don't get me wrong, what he said was helpful, but I didn't want advice during actual play.

So, as I walked to the first tee with Lord Berry one morning, I thought, *What the heck, I'll ask him nicely to leave me alone.*

Lord Berry and I, along with two gentlemen we met on the practice green, teed off on the front nine. As we walked down the first fairway, I decided it was the right time.

"Mr. Berry, I want you to know how much I appreciate all the help you've given me, but if it's all the same, I'd rather you wait until after our round to say anything about my putting."

Lord Berry looked straight ahead, answering, "It's like that, is it? Well, then I shall not be held responsible for your mid-round shortcomings."

Maybe I hadn't found the right words, but it was well worth it if he left me alone.

When we got to the first green, I noticed Lord Berry studied his wristwatch closely as we each set up to putt. It was an obvious attempt to suggest we were playing slowly. I've been called a lot of things, but never a slow golfer, and our two playing companions were at least as fast.

He did the same thing on the second green. Each time one of us addressed the ball to putt, Lord Berry looked at his watch. There we were, right on the heels of the group in front of us, and Lord Berry was quietly protesting our slow play.

Finally, I asked him, "Hey, why do you keep looking at your watch when we're putting? We can't play any faster than the group in front of us."

"Oh, do accept my unreserved apology," Lord Berry said. "But, I'm afraid answering your question would be a violation of our agreement. I will not talk to you during today's round of golf."

This man will stop at nothing to get under my skin.

Things didn't change until we got to the fourth hole, where Lord Berry finally stopped looking at his wristwatch. Instead, he pulled out a stopwatch. He putted out on the fourth green, postured himself on the fringe, and quietly pushed the buttons on his stopwatch. I could hardly believe what I was seeing.

The only good news was that our two playing companions didn't notice. In fact, one of the men made every putt he stood over. And though the other putted only so-so, I was thankful Lord Berry and his childish frolics were going unnoticed.

I finally decided to ignore him myself. After all, I'd been putting well of late, and the better I putted, the less fuel Lord Berry would have at the end of our round.

When the round was over, I stormed at Lord Berry. "You just couldn't leave me alone today, could you?"

"Spot on, Robert!" Lord Berry said enthusiastically. "Your putting is much improved!"

"Don't try to change the subject," I said. "You were doing everything you could to distract me today. And why? Because I asked you nicely to not make any on-course suggestions!"

"Indeed," Lord Berry said. "My only *suggestion* is that you keep up the good work."

Starting to soften, I said, "What do you mean?"

"Well, when I first made your acquaintance fewer than twelve months ago, you stood over every putt for approximately eighteen seconds, of which only three seconds you looked at the hole. And as you might recall, your putting was dreadful. Today, however, you spent an average of fourteen seconds over each putt, seven seconds of which you carefully studied the hole. Much improved!"

"You've gotta be kidding me. That's what you were doing? How about the other two guys?"

"Well, it's good you should ask," Lord Berry said. "As well as you putted, you were actually outdone today."

"I believe that," I admitted. "The one fellow had a bunch of one-putts in a row, and two or three birdies."

"Yes, he spent an average of eleven seconds over his putts, eight seconds of which he looked at the hole. He was extremely target-oriented and as a result, a tremendous putter."

Lord Berry never ceased to astound me. "Look, Mr. Berry," I said, "I want to apologize for..."

"No offense taken," he said, "But, you really should loosen up a bit."

I suppose I had that coming.

Journal Entry #71

Rhythm and Tempo

It's tempting, for all of us, when in pursuit of a better golf swing, to ignore the truth that we're simply not getting all we can from the swing we already have.

If a golfer can play well even occasionally, the swing is likely good, certainly workable, and what makes one day different from the next is a matter of confidence, and in turn, the tempo and rhythm with which the golfer swings.

We might all ask ourselves, particularly those among us distracted by a yearning for better mechanics, do I let go, ease through the ball and glide softly to a balanced finish? Or... do I hit at the ball with only occasional regard to the grace and rhythm with which I do so?

Further, we might all remind ourselves that good tempo can make up for less-than-perfect technique, but the best technique in the world will only work when held together by a consistently smooth manner of swinging.

Dinner At The Carrington's

Margaret turned the volume down on the kitchen radio. "Okay guys, it's time for dinner. Lucas, turn off the TV, and come to the table." She then walked to the hallway. "Roger?"

"Yes?"

"Bobby is here, and dinner is ready."

"Thank you, I'm coming."

Roger entered the dining room from the kitchen. "Good evening, Bobby. We haven't seen you since the night we came in for dinner. Please, sit down."

We shook hands before each having a seat.

"Help yourself," Margaret said. "Don't be shy."

"So, Bobby," Roger began. "Margaret and I were wondering where you went to school."

Margaret looked across the table at her husband. "Don't say 'Margaret and I.' You asked me today and I told you I didn't know."

"You mean like, where did I go to high school? I graduated in 1990 in Indiana where my father lives." I tried to remain calm, but could feel my cheeks begin to flush.

"Did you go to college?"

"No."

"Are you going back?"

"To Indiana?"

"No, to school."

"Eventually," I said. "But, it's funny you should mention school. I spend a fair amount of time at the library, mostly on days when it rains. I'm teaching myself how to write."

Roger looked up quickly, seemingly puzzled. "You don't already know how to write?"

"No, or I mean, yes, I know how to write," I said. "But I'm teaching myself to be a writer. I like to write about golf. I figure it'll give me a leg up on all the other golf professionals when I finally…"

"So, rather than taking classes, you're teaching yourself?"

"That's right."

"At the library?"

"Yes."

"You know, I see patients every day who are probably glad I didn't teach myself neurology by going to the library on rainy days. I bet they're glad I took the time to attend class, and get an actual education."

Jessica spoke up. "Dad, I already told you, Bobby is going to be a golf professional. He's working at the restaurant until his game is good enough. And, on rainy days he goes to the library to study writing."

"That's my kind of work," Roger said. "I wish I could play golf all day every day, and go to the library when it rains. Sounds more like taking it easy to me."

I remembered Jitterbug's words. *Believe in yourself, and others will believe in you. You don't have to tell Jessica or her father as much as you think you do. They'll know by your confidence.*

I ignored Roger's comments, and looked across the table at Jessica's little brother. "So, Lucas, do you play sports?"

"Not really," he said. "Why didn't you go to college?"

Jessica gave Lucas the laser beams. "Lucas, not everybody goes to college. But, not everybody has what it takes to be a golf professional either."

"Yeah, but you told Mom you never thought you'd ever like a guy who didn't go to college."

"Lucas!" Jessica shouted. "You're changing my words around!"

Margaret spoke up. "Lucas, stop trying to be hurtful."

Jessica reached over and placed her finger tips on my thigh. "I'm so sorry, Bobby."

With my best effort to smile, I lifted my balled up fists into the air, looked around, and said, "Bring it on, everybody."

The whole table laughed, except for Roger. "Bring what on?" he said. "I was just asking questions. You're not offended by that, are you?"

"No, sir."

Margaret looked at her husband. "Roger, don't you think it's time we let our guest enjoy his dinner?"

Roger seemed put off by the insinuation. "Did I say something wrong? I'm just trying to get to know Bobby."

When dinner was finally over Jessica and I retreated to the basement. "I don't know what to say," she said. "I've never had a boy over for dinner, so it was a new experience for everybody. You're not mad, are you?"

"No, I'm not mad." That was the truth. I wasn't mad at her, just battle-weary. "Your father was just asking questions."

I went home that evening wondering if it was all worth it. *Of course it is*, I thought. *I just have to keep living the life of a man working on his goal, and the rest of the world will see when the time is right.*

Journal Entry #83

The Proper Pivot

Some swing ailments consistently cause the face of the golf club to close through impact, and accordingly, create shots that fly too far left. There are other swing faults that, just as predictably, return the club in an open position, and in doing so, bring in to play the right side of the course.

However, when a golfer is just as likely to hit too far left as too far right, and cannot predict in which direction the typical miss will travel, the cause of the trouble can likely be traced back to a poor pivot.

Apparently, the golf club makes performing a proper pivot more difficult, as even the uninitiated can pivot at the hips easily when not faced with the task of hitting a golf ball.

To pivot properly, an ample amount of hip flexion is needed. If the belt buckle is pushed forward (toward the hands) at address, a proper pivot is impossible. Similarly, if the bottom of the spine, near the tailbone, is to any degree rounded instead of sharp, a good pivot will not result.

The move away from the ball is pure rotation; it's accomplished without lateral movement to the right. It is true, of course, that when the hands and arms begin to swing back, the right foot will absorb more and more weight as the backswing proceeds, but there should be no intentional loading of the right leg. Setting out to load a leg that already loads naturally makes for too much of this one thing, and in the case of the pivot, leads to a debilitating slide off center.

Having made a proper turn to the top, we must begin the motion back to the ball. The first movement down is not actually "down" at all; it is a lateral slide toward the target with the middle of the body. The hips and lower back begin the return to the ball by moving in the direction of the hole.

This much is simple. The hard part is achieving this lateral move, or "bump," without immediately unwinding the body. If, after reaching the top properly coiled, and then initiating the movement down with the lateral movement of the hips and lower back, what remains of the pivot will find the correct path.

Subtle, yet specific, this initial lower body movement represents the difference between the 275-yard tee shots of the expert, and the 200 yards the rest of the golfing world would be happy to achieve.

Chapter Ten

A long drive makes it nice, but you have to get the ball in play. If you can do both, that's great, but if there's any doubt, you'd better find a way to get that ball in play.
– Jitterbug Bell

Twin

How can you expect me to believe," I asked Jitterbug on the way across the mountain, "that Twin, a twelve-handicap player, is the toughest competitor you've ever played against?"

Jitterbug smiled as he looked out the windshield. "Oh, don't worry," he said. "You'll find out what I mean."

Jitterbug and I were on our way to play a two-man match against Jitterbug's childhood friend, Anton "Twin" Lawrence, and his partner, Duncan Braxton.

Apparently, Twin actually had an identical twin and because nobody could tell them apart, everyone called them both "Twin."

This was exciting for me. Not only would I finally meet Twin, but would basically go head-to-head with him. I considered it Jitterbug's job to beat Duncan, the club champion at Twin's course, and my job to beat Twin. And I liked our chances. After all, Jitterbug could beat nearly anyone and I'd been playing pretty well, myself. *Surely, I can beat a twelve-handicap,* I thought. But Jitterbug warned, "There's a big difference between a golfer and a gambler. Twin is a gambler. He beats players he shouldn't even be on the same course with."

After arriving at the course Jitterbug and I made our way to the driving range, where I met Twin.

"Hey, Jitterbug!" he yelled. "Who you got witchu?"

"Well, hello Twin," Jitterbug said. "This is my partner, Bobby."

Twin had a peculiar manner. He didn't really speak, but rather, laughed his words. After shaking my hand, Twin immediately started in on me. "Ooohhh, I bet Bobby can hit dat ball a long way! Can't ya Bobby?"

He then turned to Jitterbug. "But, I know Bobby can't hit dat ball as far as I can. I been hittin' dat ball hard lately, Jitterbug!"

We arrived at the first tee. Twin and Duncan won the honor and would be first to tee off. After Duncan hit a good drive, Twin turned to me. Smiling, he said, "You ain't seen nothin' yet."

I couldn't imagine a guy going on about how far he could hit the ball. If Jitterbug had taught me anything it was that yards off the tee are only helpful if you can hit it straight.

Twin moved through impact in a surprisingly fluid manner. His ball traveled about 240 yards.

"There you go, Bobby," Twin said. "See what you can do with that."

I'd show him, I thought. *On my worst day, I can fly the ball 240 yards.* I couldn't wait to see his face after I blew it past him.

But, I'll never forget the feeling I had as I put my tee in the ground on the long par four first hole. Everything went into fast motion as I measured up to the ball. I couldn't quiet my mind enough to think through my pre-shot routine. I decided it best to hurry up and hit, assuming the pieces would somehow fall into place.

I swung with all I had but caught the ball high on the heel of my over-sized driver. I looked up to see it flying weakly down the right side where it got hung up in the deep rough no more than 220 yards from the tee.

"Is that all you got?" Twin said. "I thought for sure you'd knock it way past me!"

Jitterbug smiled before hitting his drive, a beautifully controlled three-wood that propelled his ball to a flat piece of fairway just past Twin's effort.

I told myself things would return to normal but they got worse. I was already ten over par on the day when we arrived at the180-yard par three twelfth hole.

Twin smiled as he got out of his cart saying, "Ya know Bobby, I played here the other day with a guy who hit a seven-iron to this green. Knocked it pin-high too!"

I didn't consider hitting a seven-iron 180 yards to be such a remarkable task. I felt a breeze at my back as I reached for my *eight-iron. This is a chance to redeem myself,* I thought.

I closed down my short iron to squeeze as much out of it as possible. My mighty rip produced a thundering crack, but the ball flew low and left, landed on the cart path and bounced deep into the jungle guarding the left side.

When the day was over Jitterbug shot sixty-nine; Duncan, seventy; Twin, eighty; and I, an eighty-nine. Needless to say, we lost miserably.

Dejected on the way home that evening, I knew I'd let Jitterbug down, and he had every reason to find another partner. "I don't know what happened today, Jitterbug," I said. "I just couldn't seem to play golf."

"That's because you weren't trying to play golf. You were too busy trying to show Twin how hard you could hit the ball."

I couldn't deny it. Twin took me out of my game and I let him do it.

"You know, Bobby, whether you win or lose a golf match requires the cooperation of two people. To win you can either play exceptionally well, and most of the time come out on top; or, you can get a little help from the guy you're playing. I'm afraid that's what Twin made sure would happen today. He had you beat before you hit a shot."

Embarrassed, I said. "I'm sorry I let you down, Jitterbug."

Jitterbug shrugged his shoulders, apparently unconcerned about the outcome of the day's match. "You think I brought you over here to win money? I brought you here to learn, and that's exactly what you did. It may hurt right now, but you'll remember it, and that's all that matters."

A Visit From Jake

I walked into work, and stopped by the hostess stand to say hello to Jessica. Before I could say a word, she looked up and smiled. "You have somebody waiting to see you."

I looked down to the bar to find Jake staring back at me. "That's not 'somebody'," I said. "That's my buddy, Jake."

Jake got up and met me half way across the floor. "Oh my goodness," I said. "What in the world are you doing here?"

"It's good to see you, Bobby," Jake said. "I called your dad to find out where you worked, and thought I'd stop in on my way to Myrtle Beach. You think you can put an old friend up for the night? I have to leave first thing in the morning, but I thought we could hang out tonight if that's okay."

"Are you kidding? Of course!" I said. "If you want you can just hang here and watch TV at the bar until I get off, and we can have a drink after work. I have to be on the golf course at seven o'clock. You can just get up when I get up. This is awesome!"

Jake made some friends at the bar, and had more than a couple of pops in him when I finally finished my shift. "Okay Jake, I'm all done. I can't drink here but there's a bar next door. Let's hop on over there and have one?"

I could see in Jake's eyes he was nearing the danger zone, but didn't want to make a big deal out of it. We made our way past the hostess stand on our way out the front door. "Jessica, can you come next door to Magnolia's when you get off? We'll be sitting somewhere near the bar."

"I'm about five minutes behind you," she said.

Magnolias was full when we walked in, but there was a group of four ladies getting up from a small table in the middle of the lounge. "Let's snag it," I said.

Jake and I sat down before the table was cleared. Within a couple of minutes, a waitress came by, picked up the empty glasses, and asked, "What can I get you two to drink?"

"Just give me a Sprite," I said.

"Oh come on, Bobby!" Jake exclaimed. "A Sprite? Ma'am, I'll take a Jack and Coke and so will he!"

The waitress took a closer look at Jake. "Are you sure you need another drink?"

I wasn't about to wait for Jake's reply. "One drink and we're outta here," I said. "Please, two Jack and Cokes and I'll cash out with you."

The waitress pursed her lips, nodded, and walked away.

Jake clearly felt insulted. "Is she trying to say I've had too much to drink?"

"She's saying you've had the right amount," I said. "Any more would be too much. Look, let's have one and go home. You've had a long day, and we both gotta be up early tomorrow."

Jessica appeared, and pulled out the chair next to mine. "What did I miss?"

"Not a thing," I said. "Jessica, I want you to meet Jake."

The two shook hands. "Can I order you a drink?" Jake asked.

Jessica smiled. "No thanks, I'm not going to stay long. I'm sure you two have a lot of catching up to do. How long have you known one another?"

Jake's eyes rolled around in his head. "We met in the seventh grade. Best friends all through high school, but been outta contact for almost two years."

Jessica smiled at Jake. "I bet you have some good stories to tell."

I sure hope not.

"Yes I do," Jake said. "Would you like to hear one?"

Jessica sat up in her chair, smiling. "Yes please."

I tried to stop him. "Oh come on, Jake. Let's save the stories for another time."

"So, Bobby and I were at a party one night, and these four guys decided they didn't like me. One of 'em approached me and said, 'If you don't get out of here the four of us are gonna throw you outta here...'"

This is the last thing Jessica needs to hear. "Come on, Jake! That's not a good memory."

"Will you relax, Bobby? You didn't go to jail in this story."

Jessica's eyes locked on mine. "Anyway," Jake continued, "I looked up at the guy, I guess you could call him the spokesman for the group, and said, 'Four against one ain't fair.' That's when Bobby stood up and said, 'Make that four against two!'"

Jake let out a big laugh, and seemed disappointed when Jessica didn't join in. "That's right, Jessica, old Bobby here said, 'Make that four against two!'" His punchline fell just as flat the second time.

Jake glanced up, saw our waitress coming, and reached for his wallet. "Here you go, ma'am. I'll pay for the first round."

"I'm afraid I can't serve you," she said.

"But, I already told you what I wanted to drink. You said okay, and now you can't serve me? What kinda service is that?"

Oh my God, no. I motioned for Jessica to get up. "You know what? Let's just get out of here. Ma'am, I'll pay you for the drinks you poured."

The waitress shook her head. "Don't worry about paying for the drinks, just get home safe."

The waitress walked away before Jake could share any more of his thoughts on the subject. The three of us stood, and exited out the front door. *I can't believe Jake brought up jail in front of Jessica. What is he thinking?*

I opened up the passenger door to my truck. "Get in, Jake. I'm just gonna walk Jessica to her car. I'll be back in thirty seconds."

"I have to go back into Vincenzo's," Jessica said. "I forgot to clock out. I want to talk to you tomorrow. Does that work?"

"Yeah, sure, let's talk tomorrow," I said.

"Are you sure? I remember one other time we were going to talk, and...'"

"No, let's talk tomorrow. I promise."

The Glide-Stride

Smiley was on the practice green when I arrived. "Good morning, Smiley."

"Jitterbug missed you. Did you sleep in?"

"No, I had a friend from back home spend the night last night. I couldn't get him out of bed. I called the pro shop, and told them to let Jitterbug know. Did he get my message?"

"Yes, he got your message," Smiley said.

"Good," I said. "I'll try to catch him on the back nine. But, since you're here, Smiley, do you mind takin' a look at my putting stroke? I've been working on my follow through, but it just feels choppy."

"I'm afraid I can't teach you to follow through," Smiley said. "Nobody can."

"C'mon. Can't you just take a look?"

Smiley looked up from his putting crouch and leaned against his club. As if to change the subject, he said, "Have you ever noticed the way my boy, Hardpan, struts when he walks?"

I'd seen it many times. "Sure I have," I said. "Jitterbug calls it the 'Hardpan glide-stride.'"

"It's pretty smooth, ain't it? Do you think you could walk like that?"

"What? You want me to try to walk like Hardpan?"

"Yeah, let's see you walk with a cool stride like Hardpan."

I closed my eyes and thought it through. I tried to get a little rhythm as I worked my way into a full-blown glide-stride. After a few steps, I turned for Smiley's appraisal.

With an unchanged expression, Smiley shook his head. "Bobby, that might be the most ridiculous thing I ever saw. I suggest you never do that in front of people."

"What was wrong with it?"

"You got no soul, man! No attitude! You can't strut without attitude! 'Cause struttin' ain't a physical thing. Struttin' is a mindset thing! You can't fake a strut!"

"What's that got to do with putting?"

"Following through with the putter is the same way; it isn't just a physical thing. Following through is a mindset thing, and there is no way it can be faked! That's why you feel choppy when you try to follow through! Your strut looks choppy and your stroke looks choppy, both for the same reason. You're tryin' to invent it at the same time you're tryin' to do it."

"Gee Smiley," I said. "I'm afraid you lost me."

Smiley dropped three balls. "Come over here and putt these," he said, pointing to the cup some twenty-five feet away. After squaring my putter behind the first ball, he said, "Forget about the ball and just look up at the hole. Now, keep your eyes on the hole throughout the entire stroke."

I did as he said and was astounded by the result. The first two balls inched up close. The third nailed the back of the cup. As I stood in my finish position, Smiley said softly, "Look down at your putter, Bobby."

I couldn't believe my eyes. I hadn't thought a thing about my follow through, but my putter was extended beautifully in the direction of the hole. I'd followed through perfectly, and without even thinking about it.

"Now, what does that tell us about the follow through?"

"It tells us that if I'm truly focused on the target, a follow-through will appear naturally. It means I don't have to fake it."

Smiley nodded. "That's exactly right, Bobby."

"But, should I putt this way on the course? Just keep my eyes on the hole instead of the ball?"

"Probably not. You might not always make good contact. But, the good thing about golf is you have time before your shot to prepare. Use that time, Bobby. Look back-and-forth between your ball and the hole until an image of that hole gets burned into your brain. When you do, your stroke will be automatic, and you'll never have to remind yourself to follow through again."

A Secret Revealed

Jessica and I agreed "the talk" should take place in private, so she extended the invitation to her basement the following night after work. Sitting next to her on the couch, I watched and waited as she took a video cassette out of the case, walked to the TV, put the tape in the VCR, and hit Play.

I thought back on the last time I sat on Jessica's couch. "We're not going to watch the rest of *Can't Buy Me Love*, are we?"

"No, I'd rather not," Jessica said. "This one just came out on video. It's called *Boyz in the Hood.* It's the true life story of you and Jake growing up in Indiana."

Way to break the ice. "Hey, you mentioned Jake. You know, I'm awfully embarrassed about how all that went down last night."

"That wasn't your fault," Jessica said. "But I have to ask you about something. What was that he said about you going to jail?"

"Jessica, I wish I could say he made all that up, but..." There was no easy way to talk about it.

"But, what?"

"Listen, you and I grew up in different worlds. What Jake said is true, I've been in trouble. And, to answer your next question, yes, I've been arrested. Jake and Me. Public intoxication, and bein' underage to boot. Had our mug shots in the newspaper and everything. It was awful."

It was hard to read Jessica's expression; one part surprised, the other part, repulsed. "That's the way we were," I said. "Finding someone to buy us liquor and then pouring it down our throats is how we kept the cops in our town entertained. I'm not proud of it, but it's the truth, and it's a big part of why I left there. It was for reasons like what you saw last night. But, as embarrassing as that was, I'm glad Jake spouted off what he did. The weight of that secret was too much to carry around."

"What secret?"

"That I've never succeeded at anything in my life, Jessica. And then, to listen to you brag on me to your parents about how committed I am to success. I'm trying to be that person, believe me, but it's gonna take a long time, and I would've quit a thousand times by now if not for..."

Jessica reached up and kissed my lips. I didn't get to kiss back, as she was in and out in a flash. We'd exhausted the suspenseful build up, a year's wait since the memorable near-miss. Jessica stood and walked over to turn off the television. She returned to the couch before my eyes could adjust to the dark, pushed me onto my back, and said, "No more talking please."

"Any chance your father might wander down here?"

I could hear a smile in Jessica's voice. "I don't think my father would be upset if you kissed his twenty-one year old daughter. Besides, I already told you, no more talking."

The early morning hours came quickly. I woke up at 3:00 AM with Jessica's head on my chest. She slept peacefully, as if someone had removed her battery. I listened for her breathing, but couldn't hear a sound.

It was time for me to go home. I slipped out from under her and kissed her cheek before pulling the afghan to a secure spot just below her chin. "Are you warm enough?"

"Please don't leave."

"I have to."

"I know."

Chapter Eleven

Never pass up an opportunity to spend time with somebody who's up ahead on the road you've chosen.

– Jitterbug Bell

The Christmas Gift

In what seemed like a blink of an eye it was already Christmas, and I was at Jessica's house taking part in the holiday celebration.

Jessica's father had a gift waiting for me, a package of three lessons with the golf pro at Cambria Country Club, Ben Greene. "Oh, my goodness!" I said. "Thank you for this. What a great gift!"

Roger looked across at me from his place on the couch. "If you're as serious as you claim to be, then you could use the help of a top notch teacher, and Ben is the best."

I'd never heard of Ben, which didn't surprise me. He could be a world beater; but, I wouldn't know him unless he played at Muni. "Great, I will call and schedule," I said.

Roger seemed pleased. "Just so you know, Ben was a stand-out player at Duke University, and once finished runner-up in the NC State Open. Coincidentally, the guy Ben finished second to is from Asheville, too. Harold somebody, I can't remember his last name."

"Bell?"

"That sounds right," Roger said. "Yes, Harold Bell. Do you know him?"

It was Christmas, and I'd just received a thoughtful gift. This was no hill to die on. "I know he won the state open," I said.

Ben Greene

I called Ben Greene the first week of January. He told me the range at Cambria Country Club was closed until March 1, but agreed to meet me at my home range, The Practice Tee, where Jitterbug and I often hit balls.

I arrived at the driving range right on time, dragged my clubs across the walkway bridge, and hustled down to the tee. I'd never met Ben, but knew the second I saw him he was the guy I was there to meet. He just looked like a golf pro. Tall and fit with a neat appearance, Ben had an erectness to his carriage, a grace in his manner, and confidence in his place on the driving range. "You must be Ben," I said, walking up from behind.

"Bobby?"

"Yes sir, pleased to meet you."

"The pleasure is mine," Ben said.

I shook his hand, and put down my clubs. "Listen, I am so sorry, but I got called in to work, and have to leave in an hour. I know you already planned your afternoon around us being together for three hours, so I'm just going to have to eat the other two hours."

Ben smiled. "Relax, Bobby, it's no big deal. Let's just work for an hour, and we can do the other two hours later. It's probably better that way anyway. A guy can only take in so much information, you know?"

I was glad to find out Ben was a nice guy. "Okay, what do we do first?"

We had a good pre-lesson talk. I explained that I'd been playing less than three years and that my goal was to become a PGA Professional, like him. Admitting I had a long way to go, I assured him I would put the work in no matter what. After a few follow up questions, Ben asked me to hit some balls for him. "Start with something small like your eight-iron," he said. "Swing softly for a few, and then turn up the heat when you're warmed up."

Ben made some small adjustments to my posture and pre-shot routine. Nothing drastic, but before I knew it the hour was over.

"That was terrific, Ben. I really appreciate you coming out here, and like I said, if I need to absorb those last two lessons for giving you such short notice I completely understand."

"No need, Bobby," Ben said. "And, let me tell you this. If you do the work, pass your Player Ability Test, and get into the PGA apprentice program, be sure to let me know. I'm always looking for good assistants."

"Thank you, Ben," I said. "I hope to take you up on that."

Journal Entry # 96

A Tip Or Fundamental?

There is a difference between golf tips and golf fundamentals. I might compare and contrast the two.

Let's say somebody tells you to keep your head down when you swing. This may seem like a cure-all the first time you try it, but it is just a tip, and will eventually fail.

Why? Because a golfer trying to adhere to such an idea will overdo it until the tip itself becomes the fault. The golfer, trying to keep his head down, will, in time, bury his chin in his chest, believing that if a little head down is good, more head down must be even better.

Now, for the equivalent fundamental: Let's say instead you were told to keep your spine, from top to bottom, quite steady, as you turn away from, and well through your golf shot. This fundamental, unlike the aforementioned tip, has an absolute quality to it. In other words, you can't overdo it. Show me a golfer who keeps his spine too steady and you'll show me something I've not seen before. And, while it may take a moment or two longer to adopt. . . it's worth whatever time it takes to develop.

In summary, any tip that, when overdone, can lead to collapse is just that, a tip. Fundamentals, on the other hand, bring with them a more permanent benefit.

Step Four On The Horizon

The light was flashing on my answering machine when I walked in the door.

"Bobby, this is Ben Greene over at Cambria Country Club. All is well here. Listen, first I hope you're playing good golf. I haven't talked to you since, oh, I guess it was January or February when we did that lesson. I hope your golf game is coming along, and want to remind you that you still have two lessons with me. But, the reason I'm calling is to let you know there is a Player Ability Test scheduled on Friday, August 21 at Oak Valley Golf Club near Winston-Salem. Whether you think you are ready or not, you might consider signing up. It's thirty-six holes in one day, and the passing score will be

150, so two rounds averaging seventy-five or better is what you're looking for. Whether you pass or not isn't the point. It's about just getting your feet wet. If you're interested, you just need to call the PGA of America and schedule it. Let me know if you have any questions, or want to schedule those two remaining lessons. Take care, Bobby. We'll talk soon I'm sure. Bye now."

I was almost out of breath after listening to Ben's message. The thought of taking my Player Ability Test in less than four months was intoxicating. I wondered to myself, *Why wouldn't I? It can't hurt to take the test. I could possibly pass it. Why not? I've been shooting rounds in the seventies, and still had time to prepare.*

The key was to commit. *If I make my intention known. . . I will follow through with it, if only to save face.* I called Ben back, and left him a message when he didn't pick up.

"Hey Mr. Greene, Bobby here. I listened to your message, and think I will do as you suggest, and schedule my PAT. Great idea, thank you for your encouragement. I hope to be in contact soon. Thank you again, Ben!"

The Perfect Practice Round

Jitterbug invited me to play with him as he made final preparations for the Western North Carolina two-man amateur championship at Etowah Valley Country Club, the first weekend in May, 1995.

On the way across the mountain, I let Jitterbug in on the most exciting, new development in my life. "You'll never guess what," I said.

"You're probably right."

"I signed up for a Player Ability Test. It's in Winston-Salem in August. I have to shoot a couple of seventy-fives to pass."

"I think that's a great idea!"

"You know, it's not something I planned on doing this early, but it's good experience no matter how it turns out. I have to pass the test eventually so I might as well start now. And, who knows?"

Jitterbug nodded. "You're thinking along the right lines, Bobby."

Back to the matter at hand, I asked, "Are we going straight to the first tee or do you need some time to practice on the range?"

"I do all my practicing on the course," Jitterbug said.

"So what then, you're gonna hit a couple drives on each hole?"

"No, I'll just work on my chipping."

That didn't make much sense to me. After all, the tournament committee was known for stretching Etowah Valley out and letting the rough grow. It seemed to me time would be better spent grooving the driver. Nonetheless, I knew Jitterbug didn't bring me along to make suggestions.

When we got to the course, I opened the trunk to unload our clubs. I couldn't help but notice how light Jitterbug's bag was. Alarmed, I asked, "Jitterbug, where are all your woods?"

"They're in the same place as my two-, three-, and four-irons, at home in the garage."

Oh no! "Well, it might not be the same but if you want to use my long irons and woods, you're welcome to it."

Jitterbug laughed. "You think I left those clubs at home on accident? Today I will work on my chipping and when you got no long irons or woods, you can expect to have a few chip shots."

Well, it's his tournament, I thought.

After checking in, we made our way to the first tee, a 410-yard par four.

Jitterbug got to within twenty-five yards of the green with a couple of five-irons, flipped a wedge up to about four feet and willed in a par. The rest of the day went nearly the same. When Jitterbug couldn't get to the green, he'd lay up short and chip it close. On the eleventh hole, a long par three over water, Jitterbug hit a short pitch down to the ladies tee, a soft wedge to the green, and made a ten-footer for par. When the round was over, Jitterbug had hit six greens and shot seventy-three. I hit eight greens and shot seventy-nine.

On the way home I said, "Well, I see what you mean about chipping, but they'll set the course up even longer tomorrow."

"Longer for who?" Jitterbug said. "It might be longer for everyone else, but the course'll seem short to me because I'll have my woods back."

I guess that's a good point. "Speaking of your woods, are you gonna practice some driver swings before tomorrow?"

Smiling, Jitterbug said, "No, I got my driver straightened out today."

Jitterbug must've noticed the not-quite-so sure look on my face. "You see, Bobby, if you know you can chip, you don't play scared. Being scared is what makes you hit your driver in the trees and your irons in the water because you think you have to knock down the flagstick to have a chance at par. But if you know you can chip, if you're confident you can chip, if you plan to chip, you'll put a good, positive pass on every club in your bag, including your driver."

I sat back in my seat, considering it all.

"Chipping is where the game is, Bobby. I'll take the guy who can chip over the guy who can hit the ball any day."

I'd never heard Jitterbug talk so openly about his own game. Maybe he was right, chipping is *that* important. Maybe I needed to reconsider how I practiced. Or, maybe all this talk about chipping was just an overflow of euphoria from having finished the day at one over par on a 7000-yard course with nothing longer than a five-iron in his bag.

Whatever the case, it all made sense the next day when he and his partner, Pinky Paxton, went out and shot a combined eleven under sixty-one to lead the two-day event by seven shots.

Journal Entry #110

The Most Important Shot In Golf

Before a golfer should worry with any other part of the game, confidence must be absolute when putting from four feet and in. To be clear, the short putt is not the most important shot in golf, just like the layup is not the most important shot in basketball. One doesn't save a stroke for making a short putt, but rather, loses a shot for missing one.

So, if the short putt is left out of the equation on the basis that it's already in good working order, the part of the game that means the most is that which happens between four and one hundred feet. Practice in this area guarantees a return.

Shots from inside one hundred feet come in all different varieties. It makes no difference if it's a long putt, a chip, or bunker shot. Strength here will make up for mistakes elsewhere. A weakness in this area, on the other hand, will doom the player to a permanent place in the category of average.

To score well, the golfer must get the ball close to the hole from on and around the green. Provided "close to the hole" means within four feet, rolling in what's left means saving a shot. Multiply one shot by the number of times an approach shot misses the mark, and there is the approximate savings.

It's interesting how quickly the average golfer forgives himself for rarely getting the ball close when faced with a shot from within one hundred feet. He flubs the shot, curses his luck, and too quickly accepts the poor result as if it couldn't be helped. This kind of acceptance further widens the gap between one's actual and potential scoring average.

Commitment To Excellence

I arrived at just after 6:00 AM to discover something I'd never seen before. There, in front of the Muni cart barn, was Jitterbug sitting in a golf cart with his clubs strapped on the back. "What's up, Jitterbug? Are we riding today?"

Jitterbug shook his head. "No sir. We're just gonna take a little ride. Throw your clubs on the back and hop on."

I fastened my clubs next to Jitterbug's and sat down for the first time in a Muni golf cart. "What are we doing?"

"You have an important event coming up," Jitterbug said. "And, that means you have to harden your scoring muscles. Starting today, that's what you're going to do."

Before I knew it we were parked in front of the twelfth green. Jitterbug pulled a small bag of balls from his bag, saying, "Grab your sand wedge and putter."

I removed the two clubs from my golf bag, and followed along as Jitterbug walked to the center of the green, did an about-face, and paced off ten steps back toward the fairway. ". . . eight, nine, and ten," he said, then dropped a golf ball just in front of the green. He paced off another ten steps, dropped another ball, and looked back at me. "Are you coming or not?"

In just a short time, the small bag was empty, and Jitterbug had left a trail of balls, one every ten paces. "You have a ball at ten yards from the center of the green," he said. "And then, twenty, thirty, and so on all the way to this last one, which is a hundred yards." As he spoke those words it struck me that his one-yard steps were exactly thirty-six inches; his final step was within a club's length of the 100-yard plate.

"So, what are we doing?"

"I'm not doing anything," Jitterbug replied. "This is your daily buy-in, what you have to do before we play golf."

"What do I do?"

"You start with this farthest one," Jitterbug said. "It's a hundred yards. Hit it at the flagstick. Then trot on down there to the ninety-yard ball, and hit it. Then, the eighty-yard ball, and so on until you've hit all ten balls."

"So, just hit all ten balls?"

"There's two things you have to do. First, you have to get your wedge shot past the hole, and second, you have to one-putt it. When you get five out of the ten past the hole, and one-putt those same five balls, you're done for the day. One-putts from in front of the hole don't count."

"So, just five?"

Jitterbug laughed. "Keep thinkin' that."

I squared my wedge behind the first ball, and thought, *This wedge only hits the ball ninety-five yards; the hole is out of reach.* Sure enough, I took a big swing, and skulled the shot over the back of the green. "At least you got it past the hole," Jitterbug said, apparently not as irked as I.

I walked to the ninety-yard ball, and hit it dead at the flag, where it landed and stopped within a foot, just short of the hole. I waited for Jitterbug to acknowledge my laser-like shot, when reality sunk in. "That doesn't count, does it?"

Jitterbug shook his head. "Nope, it has to get past the hole."

When all ten balls were hit, I only had three qualifying balls; that is, balls past the cup. I missed all three putts. "I guess I just scored a zero."

"That was a zero," Jitterbug agreed. "Now, I'm going to the clubhouse to have a coffee and read the newspaper. I'll see you either after you score five, or the mower crew catches you, which gives you about an hour. Don't forget to fix your ball marks." At that, Jitterbug drove away.

A little more than an hour later I arrived back in the pro shop, where Jitterbug looked up before putting his newspaper down on the small table he occupied. "How'd you do?"

"The mowers caught up with me," I said. "The best I did was three. I scored a three four times."

"You'll do better tomorrow," Jitterbug said. "Let's go play."

Walking down to the tee, we discovered two foursomes already on the tee in front of us. "Oh great. We missed going off first."

Jitterbug nodded. "That's part of your training. Tournament golf is nothing like how you and I normally play. You have to learn to stay focused while you wait for the group ahead. Like it or not, that's tournament golf. You might as well count on it pretty much every day between now and your playing test. You have to learn to play well slowly."

From that day forward I performed my daily buy-in while Jitterbug waited patiently in the clubhouse. Some days, I scored five on my first attempt, and when that happened we teed off in the first tee time; but far more often, I failed to finish before the mower crew caught up with me.

It was in front of the twelfth green where I began to understand what it meant to surrender the club. It was there, too, I came to understand the meaning of true friendship. Jitterbug never once teed off before I finished my buy-in.

Pinky Paxton

Pinky Paxton spent one afternoon in May of 1995, at The Practice Tee, where he put on a clinic to support a local charity. The clinic was a smashing success, starting with his opening presentation.

Pinky asked, "Where does distance come from?" Then, depending entirely on the feedback from his audience, he'd belt long drives every way imaginable. Someone said, "Power comes from the leg drive."

Pinky smiled and replied, "You think so, huh?" Pinky pulled in a chair, took a seat, and hit a long, towering drive from a sitting position. That led to a brief discussion about the relative usefulness and limitations of the leg drive in the golf swing.

Someone else said, "Power comes from the position of your left hand on the club."

Pinky set up to the ball with only his *right* hand on the club and hit a ball 300 yards. The one-handed swing blew everybody away. It was simply unimaginable that Pinky could hit the ball farther with one hand than all but a very few could hit it with two hands. Again, the audience seemed satisfied with some brief explanation, so he moved on to his next trick.

I wasn't satisfied. I had only known Pinky for a short time and didn't want to interrupt his performance, so I waited until after the clinic to ask him about the one-handed shot.

"Bobby, have you ever played tennis?"

I played a time or two growing up. "Sure I have," I said.

"Well, can you hit a tennis ball harder with one hand or two?"

I'd never before thought about it. The only time I would consider using two hands to hit a tennis ball would be if I were attempting a backhand, and that, I figured, was because I wasn't accustomed to doing anything powerfully in a clockwise rotation. *If I wanted some sting on a forehand, I'd surely use one hand.*

"I could hit it hardest with just my right hand," I answered.

"And why do you suppose that is?"

That was a good question. Before I could come up with an answer, Pinky said, "It's all about extension. See, you might be stronger with two arms, but you can get a whole lot more extension with just one arm."

Pinky picked up his wedge and handed it to me. "Here, set up like you're going to hit a golf ball," he said. I squared up as if addressing a shot. "Now, take the club to the top of your backswing, take your left hand off and let it drop to your side."

I did as he said. "Now, swing through as hard as you can with just your right arm." It felt horribly weak.

"This time, we'll do it a little differently. Take the club back like you did before, and go ahead and take your left hand off again."

Again, I did as he said.

There was a big pause as Pinky stared at my right arm. "What's wrong?" I asked.

"Look at your right arm all folded up. Is that all the more extension you got?" I extended my right arm a little higher. "You're still not extendin'," he said.

I was on my way up higher when Pinky gripped my left shoulder and turned it until it was over my right foot. He grabbed my right arm and straightened it until it was as high up and far away from my body as it could go. "Now, swing through," he said.

From this totally extended, single-armed position, I swung through and the club made the same high-pitched swish it does when I have two hands on the club. *Oh my!* I thought. *That club zipped through impact!*

"That was awesome," I said. "How do I turn that into a two-handed swing?"

"Bobby, if you hit enough balls one-handed you'll learn more about extension than I could ever teach you."

"Like what?" I asked.

"Well, for starters," Pinky said, "you'll figure out that instead of always thinking about keeping your left arm straight at the top of your backswing, you might think about trying to keep your *right* arm as straight and extended as possible. Work on it long enough and you'll train your right arm to get in that wider, totally extended backswing position, which can only help your normal, two-handed swing. Granted, you're never gonna swing as wide with two hands as you are with one, but you've got some room in there to improve. Hit yourself a basket full of one-handed shots and see if that don't give you an extra 25 yards when you go back to two hands. I guarantee it will."

Graduation

"This is really nice, Jessica," I said. "Did you know all these people would show up for your graduation party?"

Jessica glanced at the gathering of people around the pool, and then back at the grill where her parents stood among a sea of party guests. "I didn't know what to expect," she said. "But I'm glad *you're* here."

"Thank you for saying that," I said. "But, can I ask you a question?"

"Of course."

"Does your dad have a problem with me?"

"What do you mean?"

"I mean I don't always get the best vibe from him. You know, I invite him to play golf every time I see him, and he never seems to even consider it. Yet, I know he plays almost every weekend at Cambria."

"Oh, I think that's just a Cambria thing with the doctors from work," Jessica said. "I wouldn't read too much into it."

"Okay, but when I arrived a few minutes ago he introduced me to a group of guests as 'a friend of Jessica's.' There was just something in the way he said it, like he didn't want anyone to think of the two of us as a couple."

"I will straighten that out," she said.

"No, don't say anything to him. It's not a big deal."

Jessica shook her head. "If Dad didn't like you that would be a *huge* deal. I don't think he would ever let it go; he's not the type to ever admit he's wrong about anything. But, he's never said anything one way or the other, so I think he's okay with you."

How comforting. He hasn't said anything one way or the other, so he must be okay with me? I'm not sure that's how things usually work.

JOURNAL ENTRY #119

A Sound Swing

No two players, competing at any level, present the same appearance when swinging a golf club. Yet, there are many golfers whose technique might aptly be regarded as fundamentally sound. This means that while there is some latitude to be granted, sound players simply swing within the framework of commonly regarded fundamentals.

If you move ten inches off center during the takeaway, you're going to have to move an equal amount back to the ball before impact. And, if you can do this, you may hit a good shot. But, that's not a sound swing.

Sound swingers settle up softly to the ball. They move very little off center during the backswing, and maintain a fixed tilt throughout the motion. Sound swingers finish firmly planted on the front foot, most in near-perfect balance. Sound players exude efficiency, as the output (result of their efforts) seems tremendous compared to the energy required to produce it.

Too often, golfers choose to adopt the habits of one favorite player, focusing on idiosyncrasies, mistaking individual nuances for fundamentals. Time is better spent, however, learning the set-up and swing characteristics that all great players possess. Incidentally, those are the characteristics that make up a sound swing.

Panny Bell

A scene I had only imagined in my head was about to come true. I would finally play golf with Panny Bell, known to the guys at Muni as "Hardpan."

Hardpan, who grew up under the same roof as Jitterbug, was the most storied professional to ever hail from the mountains of western North Carolina; and, Jitterbug, the most accomplished amateur. The similarities, however, seemed to end there.

I often imagined a four-day golf tournament – Jitterbug against Hardpan – and wondered who would win. I figured Hardpan would play if there was prize money involved, and Jitterbug, if the proceeds would benefit underprivileged kids. Given the stakes, each would play his heart out, and galleries would line the Muni fairways as far as the eye could see.

The wind blew hard as Hardpan and I shook hands before teeing off on the first hole at Muni. Though I knew my game, as a whole, wouldn't stack up, I was eager to see how my length off the tee compared to his. I had been shooting consistently in the seventies, which meant there were a dozen or so guys around Muni who could beat me on any given day, but there were only one or two who could hit it past me with the driver.

The first stretch of long, wide open fairways at Muni starts at the fourth hole. The wind blew directly in our face on the long par five. We both hit low, wind cheaters about 230 yards. I felt I'd drawn first blood when I found my ball had inched just past his.

"Looks like you're away," I said.

We both parred the hole and moved on to the next tee.

The fifth hole comes back to the clubhouse, opposite the fourth, which meant the same strong wind was now at our backs.

Still holding the honor, I waited for a huge gust before reaching back and taking a big swing. Again, I hit a low screamer, one I just knew would put me two up.

Don't break your back trying to catch that one, I thought.

But, to my disappointment, Hardpan walked to the tee with his old persimmon four-wood. He appeared to be bowing out, unwilling to take me on with the big stick.

Hardpan waggled and fidgeted over his ball much longer than usual. *What's he waiting for? The wind is blowing hard. He better hit it soon.* Finally, a near gale force wind turned into perfect calm. After two or three beats of deafening silence, Hardpan drew his lofted wood back and hit a shot straight into the stratosphere. Still in his finish position, he shouted skyward, "Take a ride, baby!!!"

I didn't see it come down.

We marched down the fairway to discover this time our tee shots were a little farther apart, both straight down the middle, but one some fifty yards past the other.

Hardpan walked to the shorter of the two. "I'll be damned," he said. "I woulda thought for sure that you'd be the farther one, you hittin' that big ol' driver and all, but this looks like your rock right here."

What the. . .? How could the shorter one be mine?

I hit my 125-yard approach, and then we walked to his ball. Not far away was a sprinkler head that read *81*.

I couldn't believe it. That was, and still is, the longest drive I've ever seen on the 416-yard fifth hole; and, with a four-wood.

We finished the hole and began our walk to the next tee. Curiosity was killing me. "Hardpan, how did you hit that mammoth drive back there? I've never seen anything like that."

"Bobby, I work hard on the golf course. So whenever the wind offers to lend a hand, I hit it high and let it fly."

"You didn't even use the wind," I said. "You waited until the wind completely stopped before you swung."

"That's the only way a tailwind can help," he said. "Haven't ya ever noticed that a ball going dead into the wind always balloons straight up in the air?"

"Yes."

"That's because a headwind takes whatever backspin the ball has and adds to it. Well, the tailwind does the opposite. It keeps your ball from climbing by taking all the backspin out of the shot. So ya never want to hit a shot while the wind is blowing at your back, not if you want some hang time. Ya want your ball to catch up to the wind once it's already reached its peak. That way, your ball can stay up in the air."

How in the world did you figure that out? "Wow," I said. "So, how long after the wind dies do you wait to hit your ball?"

"Oh, they's a little guesswork in there, but you can probably wait longer than you think. Believe me, it don't take long for a ball goin' 150 miles an hour to catch up to a wind that's only doin' thirty."

The Wind Wedge

The wind didn't let up during my round with Hardpan. Just the same, I enjoyed every minute of it. After I'd clearly lost the battle of the long ball, I stopped caring so much about how my game compared to Hardpan's, and began to look at the day as an opportunity to watch a great player wage war on the wind.

Speaking of wind, it blew in our face when we hit our tee shots on the par four seventh, and didn't die down for our second shots either, as we both left our approach shots some fifteen yards short of the elevated green, one beside the other. Though the pin was cut on the front edge, I wasn't too intimidated. The opposing wind would surely put some stop on my short pitch.

Precisely as imagined, my shot came to rest softly within six feet of the flag. Hardpan was known for his magic around the green, and I knew he'd do at least as well. After two or three rehearsal swings, Hardpan looked ready to take his club back, when suddenly he stopped, backed away, and took a good look around. The trees along the side of the fairway and the flagstick bending away from us confirmed what he felt. As if a short pitch to a closely cut pin on an elevated green isn't challenging enough, the wind had switched directions, and blew from behind.

Hardpan put his wedge away, and reached for his putter. He squared his blade before popping the ball, bouncing it all the way to the putting surface where it trickled to within a foot of the hole.

You gotta be freakin' kidding me. "Great shot, Hardpan."

Hardpan winked as he put his club in his bag. "Thank ya."

"I gotta tell you, Hardpan, I thought you were dead. I would have never considered using a putter."

"Shoot! That's the only way to play a shot like that. It's always easier to judge roll than it is to judge height, flight, release, spin, trajectory and roll, especially with the wind behind ya."

"Yeah, but the ball you hit didn't really roll up the hill, it looked like it bounced up."

"Oh, you gotta bounce it," Hardpan said. "You don't want that ball gettin' caught up in the fairway grass. Anytime ya usin' the putter from more than a few feet off the green, ya gotta pop down on the ball, strike it with ya hands a little ahead at impact so the ball will skip a little. If that ball starts huggin' the fairway grass, ya ain't never gonna hit it hard enough to get it to the hole."

I asked Hardpan how long it took him to get good using the putter around the green. "It doesn't take as long to figure out how to use a putter around the green as it does the wedge," he said. "I'd say ninety-nine percent of everybody oughta use the putter more often around the green. It takes the skull and chunk both off the table. Plus, it gives you a chance to stop the ball when the wind is at ya back."

Journal Entry #123

The Wind Will Blow

Of all the weather related elements suffered in golf, there is no doubt wind is the most difficult to deal with.

What about rain?

Rain is a nuisance, but the challenge it presents is only apparent. Wind has a far more disturbing effect, and no amount of it alone will relieve the responsibility one feels to continue.

The difficulty the wind presents has little to do with how a gust of air affects the flight of the ball. Rather, wind, especially a left to right wind, severs the connection between the mind and muscles, and steals a player's sense of level and plumb, making it hard to hit the ball squarely.

The shoe can rub the other way, and take a toll not on the swing itself, but on sound judgement. For example, most golfers have that one particular hole that, at one's best, can be reached with a driver and three-wood. If conditions must be perfect to reach the promised land in two mighty swings, even a slight headwind will make it a three-shot hole. Trouble comes when this fact is ignored, and the player approaches the hole with the same expectation as if conditions were ideal. The likely result is not one shot short, but rather, two. . . wayward.

The player who has a scoring standard to meet in order to stay committed, and doesn't change this standard when playing in the wind, will likely finish the day as just one in a group of also-rans. For this person reflection is torturous, as it will be discovered a score well worth its keep could've been salvaged.

It's best, when setting out on a windy course, to take things more slowly, and allow judgement, resourcefulness, and resolve to fill the vacancies left by pinpoint accuracy, deft touch, and the expectation of good bounces.

The Skyland Open

I made a seemingly awesome discovery while warming up at the range before the first round of the Skyland Open Championship, a three-day stroke play event revered as the "*Local Masters Tournament.*"

I found that if I slowed my arm swing before aggressively shifting my weight left through impact, I could release the club hard with the right hand, finish high, and hit a beautiful, towering draw, and with any club in the bag.

I scanned the range, hoping to find an awestruck walker-by who might start the buzz that young Bobby is poised to make a move in the amateur division, when suddenly, I heard the unmistakable sound of a bag dropping in the station next to mine.

"Whatssay, Bobby?"

I looked over my shoulder. "You gotta be kidding me! How in the world are you, Hardpan? I wondered if you'd make it in time to play."

"I'm good," Hardpan replied.

"Just thought I'd come down here and see which way the ball is flyin'. They got me goin' off number one today."

That made sense. Hardpan won the Skyland Open pro division the year before for a record seventh time at the age of forty-nine.

"I understand you just turned fifty," I said. "Does that mean you're gonna play in the senior division this year?"

"Well, I was hopin' to double-dip," Hardpan said. "But, they won't let me. They said, 'We don't do that kinda stuff around here.' Shoot, I don't see what the big deal is."

"What is double-dip?"

"That's where I pay two entry fees," Hardpan said. "And, play in both the regular and the senior division at the same time. I told 'em I'd play it all the way back with the young guys, but they said they ain't gonna go for it."

"So, you're just gonna play with the seniors, then?"

"Heck no!" Hardpan said. "I'm gonna play with the young guys. First place pays five hundred more dollars in the regular division."

After taking a moment to stretch, Hardpan grabbed a wedge to hit some warm-ups. His swing looked the same as I remembered, but his shots made a clunky, not-very-solid sound.

Smiling, Hardpan shook his head. "Looks like one of them days." He then grabbed a five-iron, and after seven or eight weak fades, put his club back in his bag and walked away, saying, "I guess that's it then."

I shot a first round of seventy-seven. Not particularly great considering my pre-round performance on the range. The simple sequence with which I'd begun the day, and which had produced such an elegant draw, turned into a back nine full of snap-hooks.

Again, the next day, I visited with Hardpan before teeing off. "What'd you shoot yesterday?" I asked.

"Sixty-nine," Hardpan replied.

"Sixty-nine?!? The way you were hitting the ball? You must've found your swing once you got out there."

"I didn't find nothin'," Hardpan said, putting on his glove. "My ball striking ain't been solid in months; in fact, you seen the best of it yesterday here on the range. But, I can't complain. I'm only one shot out of the lead with two days to go. A sixty-four today will put me right back in it!"

Once more, before the third round, Hardpan stopped by the practice range.

"Congratulations, Hardpan," I said. "I understand you captured the lead yesterday. Sixty-six is awfully solid."

"Yeah, I finally got some putts to drop," he said.

Hardpan swung a lofted wood four or five times before putting it back in his bag. Like the two mornings before, his shots seemed lifeless.

"I have a question," I said. "The way you're hitting the ball, you should be shooting a million, but you're leading the pro division. The *young* pro division at that. Are you just making putts or what?"

"My putting is always good," he said. "But, I think you're missin' the point on somethin' here."

"And, what's that?"

"The guy who hits the most impressive shots ain't always the winner. In fact, most of the time he isn't. The winner is the guy who does the best job of predictin' what's comin' off his club; good, bad, or whatever. That's the only reason I come to the range, Bobby, just to see what the ball wants to do. Some days it wants to go one way, and other days, another."

"But, what if it isn't doing what you want it to?"

"That's the whole point," Hardpan replied. "It don't matter what I want it to do, all that matters is what it's actually doin'. Why waste time before a tournament tryin' to make a crooked gun shoot straight? The game is hard enough without fightin' my rusty old golf swing. I don't care how ugly my action is, as long as it's consistently ugly, AND I don't try to fight it, it'll work just fine."

Hardpan won the pro division for the eighth time. Nobody seems to know for sure, but most believe it was the only time a senior won the young pro division in the history of the event.

Journal Entry #129

Hitting Too Early

There isn't a golfer among the so-called average class who hasn't at one time or another been accused of swinging too hard – too hard, too fast, too much desire. And, while I, like the rest, recognize the dangers of swinging with too much ambition, it is the misapplication of ambition that causes the real trouble.

Trying to give the ball everything one has, it's tempting to accelerate quickly from the top of the swing – this much we know.

The early hit shows up in the form of rolling shoulders, led by two hands pulling hard on the grip end of the club.

In pulling early from the top of the backswing, the spring-like whip provided by the initial bump of the hips is taken completely out, as is supportive leg drive and stored wrist cock. All in all, when pulling early, the power sources are rendered useless, and while there is great effort on the part of the golfer, there is an obvious lack of efficiency, evident to all who observe.

To put it succinctly, the problem isn't one of swinging too hard; but rather, swinging hard too soon.

The Club Championship

My career best, seventy-four, couldn't have come at a worse time. With one week to prepare for the club championship, I shot seventy-four during the tournament qualifier, which meant I would compete in the championship flight. And, as luck would have it, the day after the qualifier my trusty old driver took a sudden turn for the worst.

I played with Jitterbug the Thursday before the weekend event, and after eighteen holes of errant tee shots, I said, "Say, do you have time to look at my golf swing? I can't find the ball with my driver."

"Sure," Jitterbug said. "But, before I do I want to give you a message from Smiley. He read my copy of your golf journal. In fact, he's read the whole thing twice. He said he really enjoyed it, and thinks you should consider being a golf writer as a profession. You already know how much I like it, but I thought you should know Smiley likes it, too. And, Smiley never reads anything about golf, so that should make you feel good."

I was overjoyed. "Smiley actually took the time to read it? Twice? And, he likes it? That's so great to hear. You know, I'm thinking about giving Jessica's father a copy for his birthday. Do you think he'd like it?"

"If Jessica's father likes golf, your golf journal would be a great gift. In fact, I think he will be very impressed."

"That's what I'll do then," I said. "Okay, now about my driver. You think you could take a look?

"I'd be happy to," Jitterbug replied. "How about tomorrow?"

"Just tell me when. I have until four in the afternoon."

"Good, then meet me at the driving range tomorrow morning at eight."

I can't wait.

Jitterbug was waiting for me when I arrived the next morning. With putter in hand, he said, "How about if we have a little putting contest?"

"I thought we were gonna work on my driver. What happened to that idea?"

"Don't you worry," Jitterbug said. "Mr. Vaughn is on his way over. He'll take a look at your driver."

Even better, I thought. Reaching for my putter, I said, "What's the contest?"

Jitterbug put a tee in the ground four feet from a hole in the practice green, then dropped five balls, saying, "That's your hole."

He did the same thing four feet from another hole. "And, this is mine. Let's see who can be first to make one hundred straight putts from four feet away."

"All right," I agreed. "That'll help pass the time until Mr. Vaughn gets here."

I only made two putts before missing the first time. After that, I managed to make six in a row before missing again, and another twenty-eight before a third miss. It looked like this could take some time.

All the while, Jitterbug made his first eighty-nine before he finally missed. I couldn't help but laugh out loud as he groaned, "You gotta be kidding me!"

I got on a hot streak and managed seventy-seven before another miss. But, after another dozen or so close calls, we both had it dialed in. I was only two putts behind when Jitterbug drove the final nail with his 100th straight.

Slowly straightening up, I looked at my watch. "What time did Mr. Vaughn say he'd be here?"

"Oh, he can't be too much longer," Jitterbug said. "Of course, you said you had all day to spend. Is there somewhere you need to be?"

Not wanting to appear unappreciative, I said, "No, I was just curious."

"Well, then let's have another contest," Jitterbug said. "Let's see who can be first to chip in twenty balls. Only rule is that you can't chip into the same hole twice in a row. Chip in, then switch holes."

"Twenty chip ins? Are you serious?"

"Or, let's at least play until Mr. Vaughn gets here." As he spoke those words, Jitterbug chipped in to a hole cut only six feet from the fringe. "You better get with it. You're already one down."

I reached for my wedge and started chipping. Finally, at just after noon, Mr. Vaughn came wheeling himself to the short game area.

"Havin' any luck?"

"I've chipped in eighteen balls," I said.

"Jitterbug?"

Stroking through a chip shot, Jitterbug said, "That's number twenty right there," but his ball boomeranged around the hole.

"So, Bobby," Mr. Vaughn said, "I hear you been havin' problems with your driver."

Relieved he was finally there to help I said, "You got that right. I can't keep it in the ball park."

"Is it your driver, or is your three-wood bad too?" Mr. Vaughn asked.

"No, my three-wood is fine. It's just my driver that needs work."

Mr. Vaughn reached out his hand. "Let me see that driver."

I handed it to him and he examined it carefully. "Hmm, I see," he said. "Is this the only driver you got?"

"That's it, I'm afraid."

"Good! I'll give it back to you after the tournament." At that, he simply wheeled himself away.

There I stood, half-waiting for the punch line, half-wondering how I could have been so easily reeled in, when Jitterbug said, "Looks like you don't have to worry about your driver, not this weekend, anyway. Okay, next contest. Let's see who can be first to..."

I wish I could say I won the club championship, but I didn't. Jitterbug won. With weekend rounds of sixty-seven and sixty-eight, he captured yet another club title. As for me, not having a driver didn't hurt anything. My three-wood kept the ball in play just fine, only missing four fairways in two days. More importantly, I didn't have any three-putts. Actually, I even made a couple of long ones.

Oh, and I chipped in twice. By the way, I shot another career best, seventy-four. And, then a seventy-one.

After the tournament, Mr. Vaughn said, "A powerful swing, by itself, is never enough to win. But, sometimes, it's all you need to lose."

Tee-Time At Cambria

Following Sunday's play, which concluded the Muni Club Championship, I rushed home to get myself cleaned up and my apartment organized in anticipation of Jessica's visit. I'd turned a corner and experienced, first hand, the significance of short game magic. Still, I had to resist the urge to go on about it to Jessica. She never said anything to suggest she was annoyed by the amount of time I talked about golf, but I planned to keep it that way.

No more than thirty seconds into my first break of the day, I heard Jessica's knock. Certain it was her, I walked over to answer the door and do my best, as was our ritual, to be the better actor. First to deliver my monologue, I said, "I coulda been a contender. Instead I'm just a bum."

Straight faced, Jessica shook her head. "Bobby, that was so bad I forgot what part I was about to act out."

"Did you at least recognize my part?"

"You were *trying* to be Marlon Brando in *On the Waterfront*. You left out, 'I coulda had class.'"

"I was paraphrasing."

"Yeah, I'd like to hear you tell a director that. Oh well, at least you're good at golf. Speaking of which, how did the tournament go?"

"Jitterbug won. Again."

"What about you?"

"I finished second," I said. "But, it wasn't even close. Jitterbug beat me by ten shots."

Jessica perked up. "Oh, I'm supposed to ask you a question for my Dad. He wants to know if you can play golf with him at Cambria on Sunday, August 20th, at nine in the morning."

"That's the day before my PAT," I said. *And, the third anniversary of the day Carrie left for Tulane.*

"Oh, that's right! Your big day is coming up. Should I tell him it's not good for you?"

"Are you kidding? I'd love to play golf with your dad. And, by the way, I have something I want you to give him."

"What's that?"

I went back to my bedroom, and returned with the present I'd painstakingly gift-wrapped for Jessica's father. "I know your dad's birthday is this Thursday. Can you give him this, and tell him I said, 'Happy birthday?'"

"You're so nice!" Jessica said. "What is it?"

"I guess you could call it my manifesto on golf. I typed out my first hundred and thirty journal entries. You said he reads golf books, so I thought I would..."

"This is wonderful!! He will love it!"

God, I sure hope so.

The Four-Wood

Jitterbug agreed to join me one Sunday afternoon for nine holes, but only on the condition we'd each select one club, with which we'd tee off, putt out, and hit every shot in between. I chose my seven-iron, and Jitterbug, his four-wood.

Jitterbug shot even par, thirty-six, for nine holes with just his four-wood. To me, it was simply amazing. To him, it seemed like no big deal, as he considered it nothing more than a good way to practice.

"The reason so many people stop improving after a few years," he said, "is they stop thinking about what the club is doing. All they think about is what their body is doing. When you've got just one club, you're forced into thinking about what the club must do to create all the different shots."

He said it also makes you think about where you want to hit your ball. For example, it's natural to wonder how Jitterbug could blast out of a bunker and make it stop with a four-wood. He couldn't. Nor could he hit a soft pitch to a tight flag. But it didn't matter because he knew he couldn't, so he never put himself where he had to.

Jitterbug only hit two greens in regulation the day he shot thirty-six; one, a par five he reached in two shots, and the other, a 188-yard par three. The remaining seven greens he missed, he missed on purpose because he knew he couldn't hold the green with a four-wood. He simply shot to the side and used his four-wood to chip up close. But, he carefully selected the side on which he missed. He didn't leave himself with a flop shot or an extremely grassy lie with which to contend. He made sure each leave offered an adequate amount of green to run the ball to the hole.

"Every shot in golf," he said, "should be designed around the idea of making the next shot easier. The average golfer can't see the significance of that with all fourteen clubs in the bag. He thinks that no matter where he leaves himself, he's got a club that'll get him out. But, it ain't so. You tell me how many people are good at diggin' the ball out of deep rough and then make it behave perfectly once it hits the green. There's not a club in the world that will make the combination of long grass and a tight flag easy to deal with."

I asked Jitterbug how his mindset changed when he played with all fourteen club versus playing with just his four-wood. "I'll hit more greens with all fourteen clubs," he said. "But, the mindset is still the same. I still play every approach imagining that if I miss the green, the only club I have to chip with is my four-wood. If I do that, I'll never shoot for flags tucked tight behind bunkers, back on a tiny shelf, or cut close to the edge of the green. Of course, I'll have some long putts playin' that way, but I'll take a long putt over a tight, grassy chip any day."

Journal Entry # 132

That Something Else

Touch and technique are so closely related it's hard to know which is more important. Furthermore, can either be improved without the other, or is there a third element?

To explore the subject, let's suppose you are a beginner player, and somehow you and a friend find yourselves stranded on a desert island with nothing more than a sand-wedge, a practice green and as many balls as you can chip and pitch.

My guess is that without any instruction, and probably within just a few days, your ball contact would improve dramatically, so much you may say, "Hmm, I'm starting to develop some touch. This game must be all about 'touch.'"

But, soon after, your island-mate may say, "I can tell you've gotten better. You're not rocking back-and-forth when you swing like you did before."

Isn't that telling? In a short time, whether consciously or not, and without any words of advice, you stopped swaying back-and-forth during your swing, an indication of better technique.

So, the question remains, "Is it touch, technique, or is there still something else?"

It could be the latter. As touch and technique grow together, they bring about a third quality, which I call "golf poise."

Poised golfers are smooth. Whether faced with a four-foot putt or a sixty-yard pitch, poised players have no jerks, jabs, or jolts anywhere in their motion.

Equally striking, poised players are balanced, especially at the finish. Sure, many golfers address the ball with balance, but only those with golf poise maintain balance through to the finale, which makes poised players appear calm, relaxed, and unhurried.

So, while touch and technique each provide lift for the other, they are only rungs on the ladder to unshakable poise.

MOM'S LOVE

Mom and I hadn't talked about golf in more than a year. In fact, we didn't discuss any topic that might lead to a discussion about golf. I thought of it as our own little "Cold War," and understood the wall between us wouldn't be torn down until I either gave up golf or succeeded at it.

"Sorry I'm late, Mom."

"No problem," she said. "You've been much later than this many times."

Mom was about to have a new couch delivered, and needed her old one moved to the basement.

"Bobby, do you know we have a mutual acquaintance?"

"Oh yeah? Who?"

"Scott Rhodes."

"No kidding? How do you know Scott?"

"His wife is a nurse on my floor. We all had dinner last night."

Scott Rhodes was a Muni member. We were friendly, but didn't usually end up in the same group. He golfed later in the day, so on the few occasions when we played together it was usually my second round of the day.

"Do you know what he said about you?"

Here it comes. "No, I don't, Mom."

"He says you're trying to be a golf professional, and that all you do is play golf all day every day."

"Was that news to you, Mom?"

"No, but what he said next was."

"What was that?"

"He said when he first met you, you were so bad most people didn't want to play with you. He was sure you started too late to ever be good."

"I did start late, Mom. You know that. I don't expect anybody to believe in me."

"Bobby, he said he's since changed his mind. He said you're an excellent golfer, and you just finished second in the biggest golf tournament of the year."

I was ready for the shoe to drop. "And, did you tell him what you thought, Mom?"

"Yes, I did. I told him you'll finish first next year."

I hadn't hugged Mom so tightly since I was a little boy. "That made me very proud, Bobby. I'm very proud of you."

Chapter Twelve

It's a mistake to be one person in a crowd and
a different person when you think nobody can see.
Your character follows you everywhere you go.
– Jitterbug Bell

Carrie's Call

Jay approached me at the coffee station. "You know you're not supposed to receive personal phone calls at work, don't you?"

"Yes, why?"

"You have a call waiting on line two. Make it quick."

I made my way down the stairs to pick up the phone and tell whoever it is they better never call me at work again.

"Hello?"

"Bobby?"

"Yes, who's this?"

"It's Carrie." This was no joke. I recognized her voice as soon as she said my name. "I know you're at work and I'll make it quick. I'm coming through Asheville tomorrow and wanted to see if you were up for a visit."

"Where are you now?"

"I'm in Atlanta with some girls from my golf team," she said. "Are you going to be around tomorrow? And, if so, are you free?"

A flood of excitement came rushing in. *I'd love it if Carrie could see me play golf. We could meet at Muni for a quick nine holes. What would it hurt to have a visit? I'd bet Jitterbug would be impressed with Carrie's swing. She'd be back on the road again, and nothing would ever come of it. Jessica wouldn't even have to know.*

"Sure, I'm around," I said. "But, I'm afraid I'm not free. Look, I'm not trying to be mean, but I can't receive calls at work, so I have to hang up. Safe travels, I gotta go."

I hung up the phone, turned, and found myself face to face with Jessica. "Who was that?"

I hesitated long enough to read Jessica's expression. "It was, uh, you know. . . Carrie."

"Do you mean as in Indiana Carrie?"

"Yes."

Jessica backed up a step, and turned to look at the reservation sheet. "I heard what you told her."

"What did I tell her?"

"You told her you're not free. Thank you."

I finally exhaled. "No need to thank me, Jessica. I love you." Those words erupted from an honest part of my heart, but seemed to echo, and felt out of place. "Or, I mean, I love that you..."

"Stop right there. What did you just say?"

"I said, 'No need to thank me.'"

"After that."

"Which part?"

"Did you just say you love me?"

It was time to surrender. "Yes, I think it was me who said it."

"Was it an accident? Or, did you mean it?"

"Can't it be both?"

"Do you know you've never said that to me before?"

"Yes, and this time was an accident."

"Well, this isn't. I love you, too."

Journal Entry #137

Consistency

There are many teachers across the land who are quick to suggest the average golfer should give more attention to the correct moment-of-impact position, and less to the wind-up and unwinding.

I suppose there is no way to deny that an unpolished, flailing motion is capable of delivering the club squarely to the ball. Still, the operator of this kind of swing will not reach full stride until his swing, through intelligent practice, routinely travels on a more deliberate, time-tested path.

An effective forward stroke results in powerful, square contact between the club and ball. This is the telling moment of the swing. The purpose of the backswing is simply to take the golfer into a position from which this effective forward motion can most easily occur.

The proper backswing, therefore - for the purpose of consistency - deserves as much attention as the proper impact position. The correct swing is really just a correct sequence, occurring naturally without need for redirection or compensation.

Chapter Thirteen

The fact we're all going to die means we have to make choices. We have to decide how to spend our precious time here. Knowing we can't live forever is what makes us all live different lives.
– Jitterbug Bell

Smiley's Wedge

Smiley Bell died in his sleep on August 12th, 1995, at the age of ninety-one.

Jitterbug and I spent the late evening after Smiley's funeral hitting short shots around the twelfth green. Walking back to our cars at dark, Jitterbug said, "It doesn't look like Smiley will be needing his old wedge anymore."

"I guess you're right. But, it won't be any use to you. Smiley was the only one who knew how to use it."

Jitterbug stopped beside his car. "That's true enough, Bobby. But it's okay, I like mine better anyway."

I thought back on my first ever encounter with Smiley. I remembered using his wedge to nervously chip balls onto the twelfth green.

"It must've been a hundred degrees out when I first met Smiley. He had a pile of golf balls, and one after the other..."

My thoughts were interrupted when Jitterbug reached in the

back passenger side window of his car, and pulled out Smiley's wedge. "Bobby, Uncle Smiley wanted nothing more than for you to make it as a pro."

"Really? Why?"

"I can't really say for sure. But, I think it's because every time you left, well. . . you came back. You wouldn't stay gone. I suppose it's easy to pull for somebody like that."

"Wouldn't stay gone? What do you mean?"

"Well, Uncle Smiley told me about you during breakfast the morning after your first meeting. He told me he'd assigned you to a week of standing on one foot to hit chip shots, but was sure he'd never see you again."

"Why wouldn't he see me again? I mean, the way he chipped those balls. It was magic. He just..."

"I know. I've seen it before."

Jitterbug paused to look back at the twelfth green. "But, what I hadn't seen before was the glimmer in his eye, the glimmer you provided, a week later when you came back. There you were again, your clubs on your shoulder, walking down to where you said you'd be, and Smiley couldn't believe it. I mean, the man had you written off. Said there was no way you'd show up again."

Jitterbug turned to face me. Softly nodding, he smiled. "But you did, Bobby. You showed up."

Jitterbug's eyes clouded as he handed me Smiley's wedge. "Don't you ever forget what it means to show up."

Journal Entry #141

The Measure of a Man

Smiley Bell was a fine golfer, an exceptionally gifted player, who combined the shotmaking skill of Gene Sarazen with the rhythmic grace of Gene Kelly. Yet, to all of us at Muni, upon hearing of Smiley's passing, it wasn't his golf swing we talked about. Rather, it was the sincerity we felt when he said, "Good morning," or the compliment it was to hear him say, "Good shot."

Smiley was a big man, not in physical stature, but big in the greater sense. He could hit a short pitch over a deep bunker to a tight pin, or years before that, intercept a line drive on its way to left centerfield, and turn a sure double into double-play. Yet, despite it all, he'll be remembered most for the kind gentleman he was.

This week's lesson is a lesson for life: We tend to judge how well we play as the measure by which we make an impact, but others remember us by how we make them feel.

Smiley, thank you for what you did for me. I will live my life in honor of your memory.

Cambria Country Club

Two years had gone by since I passed up my first invitation to play Cambria Country Club, but the day had finally arrived.

Pulling into the long drive in front of the clubhouse I took a moment to reflect. It wasn't Magnolia Lane at Augusta National, but it was a giant step in that direction.

As eager as I was to play Cambria, what I wanted most was to earn Roger's approval. It had been nearly a month since his birthday, and Jessica hadn't said anything to indicate whether or not Roger even opened the gift I'd given him. The way I figured, either he didn't read what I wrote, or he didn't enjoy it enough to mention it to Jessica, and neither was a positive sign. Still, I couldn't give up.

The outside service staff members greeted me at the bag drop. One young fellow reached in the back of my truck and removed my clubs, as another opened my driver door. "You can just leave the keys in it," the young man said. "Here is your voucher."

Valet parking? I don't want this. "I'm sorry, what?"

"I will park your car for you."

This is unnecessary. I need a moment to organize myself. "No thanks," I said.

"I'm sorry, sir, but we don't offer open parking."

A voice called out from behind me. "Hey Bobby, the tee time is under Carrington." It was Jessica's father.

The valet attendant looked irritated. "He doesn't want to valet park. I told him that's his only option."

Roger walked to my door. "Come on, Bobby, just let him take your truck. I'll pay for it, it's no big deal."

"It's not a matter of paying for it. I just wasn't expecting it. All I need is a second or two and I'm good." Roger didn't hear a word of my explanation, as a sudden blow of a car horn sounded off from a vehicle two back from his.

"Hey, move your cars, will ya???"

Roger smiled. "That's Troy, our playing partner. He's a real character." The valet attendants soon drove off with our cars, and the three of us stood waiting for our golf carts. "Bobby, I want you to meet Troy Campbell."

Troy was about the same age as Roger, late forties or early fifties. "Nice to meet you, Troy."

Troy reached out and gave me an exceedingly firm handshake. Not ready to let go, he pulled me in close, and said, "This place has to be a step up from that goat pasture you play. I don't know how you feel like you fit in at Muni."

I stammered out what I could. "Yes, Muni isn't like this, I mean it's fine for me, but this place is amazing." Troy's energy was awful.

The service staff brought up our golf carts within just a couple of minutes. Roger got the attention of a staff member, and pointed to my bag. "Put that one on the passenger side of my cart. Bobby, you can ride with me. Troy, it looks like you're riding solo today."

"Isn't that sweet?" Troy said. "You two can talk about how Bobby is gonna get his legs broken if he doesn't treat Jessica right." This made for an awkward, uncomfortable moment. "Oh, and that reminds me. I heard this one the other day. When does a Mexican become a Spaniard?"

Roger and I looked at one another and then back at Troy for the punchline. I shrugged my shoulders, as Roger said, "I don't know."

"When he marries your daughter," Troy said, erupting in laughter. I didn't get it, and was thankful Roger didn't laugh either. "Come on you two, will you lighten up?"

"You gentleman enjoy your round," the younger of the two outside service members said. All loaded up, we rode off in the direction of the driving range. Turning the corner away from the front drive, Roger said, "Troy is an acquired taste, but he's been a good friend. I have him to thank for my membership here. He recommended me to the committee and since he's a member in good standing my application was accepted; in less than two months I was approved. I've been here three years now."

I thought about how different this was from my experience at Muni. I didn't need a recommendation to become a member. There was no committee to review applications and accordingly, no granting or denying one's acceptance. There was no pain-in-the-butt valet parking. I could just walk on, and do so without hearing a distasteful, racially motivated joke that wouldn't be funny even if I lacked basic social decorum. Roger pulled up and parked next to the range, saying, "We still have a few minutes. Grab whatever clubs you want and let's go warm up."

"If it's ok with you, I'm just going to go chip a few," I said, motioning toward the practice green.

"Is that Bobby over there?" I looked over my shoulder to find Ben Greene walking in our direction.

"Hey Ben, great to see you," I said.

"How's your game?"

"Pretty good. You know, I've dropped six or eight shots since February." That wasn't a lie. I didn't say it was due to his help, but it wouldn't hurt if he thought so, especially on his turf in front of his members.

"That's great news," Ben said. "Listen, you still need to come take your golf lessons."

Roger was searching for a golf glove in the bottom compartment of his golf bag. Suddenly, he stood up straight, and asked, "Say, Bobby, didn't you tell me you already took those lessons? I asked you and you said you'd already met with Ben."

Before I could answer, Troy interrupted, laughing and pointing at Smiley's wedge. "What is that thing in your hand?"

I didn't want to talk to Troy about Smiley's wedge, Muni, or anything else near and dear. "I'm going to go hit some chip shots before we play."

Troy swiped the club from my relaxed, unguarded grip. "Let me see that thing." He lifted the clubhead end, examined the grooves on the face, and dropped a couple of range balls. "What an old piece of junk this club is."

Troy placed my most cherished possession behind a golf ball and was about to make a backswing when I reached down, grabbed the club with both hands, and snatched it back into my control. "No sir, that's not your club."

Troy seemed incredulous. "What the hell? I just wanted to see how the old club hits."

"It doesn't do anything by itself."

There was an uncomfortable pause, which came to an end when Ben pretended to cough. "Enjoy your round, gentlemen."

If this is the private club experience, I'll take Muni any day. I wished I hadn't accepted the invitation. More than that, I wished Jessica's father would tell Troy to go to hell. Further, I wished Roger wasn't Jessica's father so I could just leave. Instead, I took three balls to the chipping area. The job now would be to tranquilize my heart rate, remember to smile, and appear unbothered.

Within minutes we were on the first tee, where I blasted a drive straight down the middle of the fairway, leaving myself a nine-iron approach to the 425-yard first hole.

Walking off the eighteenth green, some four hours later, Troy extended his hand. "Good round, Bobby. Do you have time for lunch?"

"Of course," I said. "That would be nice."

The three of us made our way into the clubhouse, turned left, and walked down a huge corridor with two walls decorated by old, framed pictures. Among them were photos of Bobby Jones, Walter Hagen, Gene Sarazen, and Ben Hogan. The one that had my attention, however, was of Lou Gehrig and Babe Ruth, all dressed up in golf attire, pictured with two caddies holding umbrellas above the Yankee sluggers' heads on what was obviously a rainy day at the course. I stopped, astonished by the clarity of the photo. Never had I seen a depiction from that era so sharp and full of detail. "Were all these pictures taken here at Cambria Country Club?"

Troy paused and looked back at the wall with the boastful expression of a man about to brag. "Yes, all those famous golfers played here at Cambria. It's not every day you visit a club that has this quality lineup of past players."

"Wow, this is really cool," I said. "Even Babe Ruth and Lou Gehrig played here. What a great picture." Despite my awestruck gaze, the observation left my two hosts unresponsive. *Not everybody likes baseball*, I thought.

Roger pulled open the door at the end of the hallway. "The guest lockers are on the right, Bobby. Member lockers are back the other way. What do you say we all get cleaned up, and meet here in twenty minutes?"

"Okay, but I don't really need a locker. I just need to change out of these spikes. My other shoes are in my truck, so I'll walk out there and change."

"That works," Troy said, pointing to the far end of the locker room. "We'll meet you down in the grill after we get a shower then. Should be about twenty, no more than thirty minutes."

I couldn't believe these two were going to take a shower before having lunch. This was a completely different culture than I was used to, and one I didn't find all that attractive. *What would Jitterbug think if I insisted we showered before sitting down for iced tea? He'd think I was crazy.*

Walking to the valet I began to consider my appearance. *If these guys are taking a shower, I better at least take off my cap, comb my hair, and wash my face.* I approached the attendant. "Pardon me, I don't need my car, but I need to get my shoes."

"Do you have your voucher?"

I read him the number on the ticket. The young attendant reached over, pulled my keys from a hook, and tossed them to me. "It's no problem," he said. "You can go get your shoes."

"I don't even know where you took my car," I said. The attendant pointed to a lot just below the front drive. "Got it, thanks."

I changed my shoes, and made my way back to the guest locker area where there were towels, soap, deodorant, and a bowl of combs soaking in disinfectant. I was thinking how nice the whole arrangement was when I heard Troy's voice from the other side of the of a nearby row of lockers. "Didn't you say he quit college to become a waiter at Vincenzo's? What kind of a future is that?"

He's talking about me.

Roger replied, "He never even started college. I think he's trying to be a golf professional."

'You think?' Oh thanks for sticking up for me! What do you mean, 'You think?'

"A golf pro? Hell, he's good, but he ain't *that* good."

I just beat you by 18 shots. And, if I'd used my own wedge instead of Smiley's I would've beaten you by more than that.

"We'll see," Roger said. "He's got his playing test coming up tomorrow."

"Never mind all that," Troy said. "How about the way he snatched that wedge out of my hands in front of Ben Greene? Who the hell does that? I've never seen Ben act that way. In fact, we should ask Ben what he thought about it."

"I know," Roger said. "I'm trying to forget that happened."

Forget what happened? That Troy called Smiley's wedge a piece of junk? Or, that I wasn't about to let that bigot use it to hit a golf ball? Which are you trying to forget?

"While you're at it," Troy continued, "maybe you should forget that he lied to you about taking lessons from Ben. He lied straight to your face."

I didn't lie. I scheduled three, but had to leave after an hour. But, Ben, because he's a decent guy, is willing to honor the two remaining hours.

"I was surprised by that," Roger said. "I just can't help but think if he was really serious about golf he would've jumped on the opportunity to work with Ben."

Jitterbug teaches me. And, Mr. Vaughn. You're sold on Ben because he finished runner up in the N.C. State Open. If that's the measure of a teacher, which it isn't, then maybe you should consider Jitterbug won the state open four times! Except I would never tell you that because I don't want to appear unappreciative of the gift you gave me.

"One more thing," Troy said, "and I don't mean to beat the guy to his knees, but how stupid does he think we are? Who did he try to say was in that photo out there? Babe Ruth? Hell, Babe Ruth was a baseball player. The guy says he's going to be a golf pro and he thinks Babe Ruth was a golfer. He's just full of hot air. I'm sorry, Roger, but it must be hard for you knowing this guy is dating your daughter."

George Herman Ruth, born February 6, 1895 in Baltimore Maryland, nicknamed Babe, was pictured on the wall next to Henry Louis Gehrig. Gehrig died at 38 of amyotrophic lateral sclerosis, referred to now as Lou Gehrig's Disease. They were members of the 1927 Yankees, known in baseball circles as the original Bronx Bombers. Yes, they were baseball players, two of the greatest, but they played recreational golf, and are on the wall in there. Who doesn't know Babe Ruth when he sees him? To anybody who follows sports the shape the Babe's face is more recognizable than Alfred Hitchcock's.

I held my breath, waiting for Roger's response. *Go ahead, Roger, tell him I'm good to your daughter... Tell him my intentions are honorable... Tell him, Roger, I'm waiting...*

"I'm going to have a talk with Jessica," Roger said. "She's not going to like what I have to say, but she'll just have to come to terms with it."

All the good in the world disappeared in an instant. My hopes, my dreams, my desire, my resolve to carry on. . . all gone in the time it took Roger to utter two sentences.

There was no place for me to hide. I cleared my throat, took a deep breath, blew it out, and walked around the corner to face my two accusers. "Gentlemen, thank you for having me out for golf. It was a pleasure and I appreciate your generosity. As it turns out, I just didn't budget enough time to sit down and have lunch." At that, I walked out the locker room door, turned right, and began my stride down the picture-lined hallway.

It didn't matter how well I played today. This was never about golf. Roger brought me here to humiliate me.

I knew this would happen.

I knew it.

*****

Troy opened up his menu. "Do you suppose Bobby heard what we said? You know, we were just talking, we really didn't say anything that wasn't true."

Roger stared straight ahead. "I don't think it's a question of whether or not what we said is true. If he heard us I'm sure he's hurt."

Troy shook his head. "Oh well, the truth hurts sometimes. Now what the hell is taking that waitress so long? Are we invisible?"

Roger folded up his menu and pushed himself away from the

table. "Troy, I'm afraid I'm a little bit like Bobby and didn't budget enough time for lunch. I have things I need to do, I'm sure you understand."

"Oh, come on! You're just going to leave me to eat alone? What's the matter? Just stick around! You gotta eat!"

Roger stood up from the table. "No, I don't," he said. Roger placed both hands on the back of the chair before pushing it under the table. "I need to get out of here. Margaret and I are leaving for a four-day trip to the lake house this evening and I still have things to get ready before we hit the road. Thanks for golf. It was memorable."

Roger stopped by his locker to gather his wallet, keys, and golf visor. Possessions in tow, he pulled open the big, heavy door leading to the corridor with all the photos lining the wall. Peering down and then up, he found himself chest to chest with Ben Greene.

"Oops, excuse me," Roger said. "I wasn't looking where I was going."

"Not at all. How was your round?"

Roger tried to smile. "It was good."

"Glad to hear that. Tell me, did Bobby enjoy the course? You know, he's got his Player Ability Test tomorrow."

"He played well; shot sixty-eight today."

"Wow, sixty-eight?!? He said he was doing better, but I didn't expect to hear that."

"Yeah, and that's with a double bogey," Roger said. "He stubbed two chips in a row with that old wedge he plays with."

"That's a good score," Ben said. "A really good score."

Roger paused before asking, "Say, Ben, as long as we're on the subject of Bobby, did he ever talk to you about golf lessons?"

"Yes, he did. We met way back in February as I recall. Had a good lesson. I think we did an hour and you know how things are, time gets away and we still haven't scheduled the other two. He's probably saving those lessons for when he needs them. Wow, sixty-eight today! Whether or not he passes tomorrow, he's getting close. He'll be starting his three years of school soon enough."

"What three years of school?"

"The playing part is just a qualifier," Ben said. "After that there's three years of training. Once he gets through school he'll have a good career to look forward to. There are 15,000 courses in the country, and they all need a good pro."

Roger nodded. "Thanks, Ben. I was only curious. You have a good day."

Ben smiled. "You too."

Starting his walk away, Roger's attention was captured by a framed photo on the wall. "Wait a second, Ben. Can you tell me who's in this picture?"

Ben walked over to have a look. "Believe it or not, that's Babe Ruth," he said. "And I can't remember who the other guy is, but I think he was a baseball player, too."

"Lou Gehrig?"

"Yes! That's exactly who it is. Lou Gehrig. I'd forgotten his name but that's Lou Gehrig."

"Thank you, Ben. I'll see you soon."

*****

Jessica showed up at my apartment an hour early, dressed for dinner. Answering her knock, I was in no mood for the comedy sketch greeting we'd both become accustomed to. "Hi, how are you?" I said. It occurred to me, only when my eyes met hers, whatever expression I wore would likely be mistaken for a funny act, which made things difficult.

Jessica reached up and grabbed my shirt below the neckline,

pretended to ball it up in her tight fist, and in the voice of a 1930's Hollywood gangster said, "You look here, see? Do you know what I do to guys like you?"

I looked at her blankly. "No, I don't."

Jessica softened her grip, kissed my cheek, and said, "I straighten their collar." At that, she used her palms to iron down the slight wrinkle she'd created. "How was golf with Dad?"

"It was fine."

"Let me guess. Paul Newman in *Cat on a Hot Tin Roof*?"

"I never saw the movie."

"You would love it. Paul plays the part of an ex-football star who's mad at the world because his gay lover committed suicide, and his wife, played by Elizabeth Taylor, can't understand why..." Jessica took a step back and looked deep into my eyes. "Either you're acting right now or something is wrong. Please be normal for a second."

"There's nothing wrong. I'm fine."

"Oh no. What happened?"

"Nothing happened. We had a good round of golf."

"Who'd you play with?"

"Your Dad and Troy Campbell."

"You're kidding me!" Jessica exclaimed. "Dad invited Troy Campbell to play with you? I can't stand him. He's the reason I never go to the club. He's awful. No wonder you look so beaten down."

"Look, Jessica, I'm sorry, but I was about to call you. I have my PAT tomorrow and I need to get some rest tonight. It's a two-hour drive over there, and I'm meeting Jitterbug at 5:30 tomorrow morning at Muni so we can ride together. It's thirty-six holes; I just need to rest tonight. I am sorry if...."

"Bobby, please, it's okay," Jessica said. "I totally get it. I should've called before just showing up. My parents left for the lake house this afternoon and won't be back until Wednesday. If you want to come over after you finish tomorrow I would love to see you. More than anything else I just want you to play well. We have all the time in the world after that."

I wish that were true.

Chapter Fourteen

If it's golf, the plain variety, you're referring to, yes, it's a test of who can best swing the club. If, on the other hand, you add wind and rain, it's a test of resolve.

– Lord Berry

The Player Ability Test

One can only gain acceptance into the Golf Professional's Training Program by shooting a pre-determined target score. The score for this particular course, Oak Valley Country Club, near Winston-Salem, was 150 for thirty-six holes, which meant a pair of seventy-fives would be good enough to pass. Not an easy task in casual play, but considerably more difficult when sent out with a pencil and scorecard.

To add to the stress level, the weatherman predicted hard rain and there was no way to know how much wet weather we would endure before play would be suspended.

We eventually found out.

Standing beside the practice green, waiting for our tee time, Jitterbug said, "Bobby, I believe you told me your parents split up when you were eight years old. That's when you and your mom moved here to Asheville. Do I recall that correctly?"

"Yeah, why do ask?"

"And, your father used to send you boxes of baseball books. Is that right?"

I'd never told Jitterbug about the baseball books. "How do you know that?"

"Your mother came by Muni yesterday. She wanted to surprise you, and watch you play a few holes. Of course, you were at Cambria with Jessica's father, but Stan Watkins asked her to stick around so she and I could meet. She's a very nice lady, Bobby."

"And, you talked about my baseball books? How did that come up? You two just met."

"It was because I asked, Bobby. I wanted to know how you could recall the names of baseball players from a hundred years ago like I can name my first cousins. I always suspected the answer to that question has to do with this golf pursuit of yours."

"Yeah, I used to read about baseball. I guess maybe I never told you because I didn't like how the story ended."

"Was reading those books something you did for your father?"

"Is that what my mom said?"

"No, she didn't. I'm asking you."

If anybody deserved to know the truth, it was Jitterbug. "Dad and I played every day before Mom moved us away. Then, Mom worked evenings, so I had no way to get to practice. No more being with my Dad, and no more playing baseball."

"But, you eventually moved back with your father, right? When was that?"

"Four years later, but by then, everything was different. I hadn't played the whole time I was away. I couldn't hit a baseball if the coach tossed it to me underhanded. It was humiliating. That's why I can't stop until I'm a golf pro, Jitterbug. I have to show Dad I'm not still that kid sitting on the bench."

"Why did you read those books, Bobby? I'm curious. Was it because you wanted your dad to know how much you missed him?"

This didn't seem like the time to dwell on the past. "Yeah, I guess so," I said, "but, what's this about? Why do you want to know about my dad and baseball?"

"You're playing with Smiley's wedge in the most important golf event of your life, and I'm trying to figure out why. Is it because you want Smiley to know how much you miss him?"

I didn't see this coming. There, in my fingers, at the end of my hanging left arm, was Smiley's wedge.

Jitterbug took in a deep breath. "Bobby, I know you want to honor Smiley, and I appreciate that. But, the best way you can honor Smiley is to play for you today, not for him."

"But Smiley is the reason I..."

"Smiley is gone, Bobby, but he gave you a gift. Now, it's time to use that gift. You put in the work, and you did it with your wedge, not Smiley's."

Jitterbug reached out his hand. I met him half way and handed him the six-decade old club. He gazed down at the wedge we both cherished, then back up at me. "This wedge is for something else, Bobby. Let me have it, and I'll bring you back the one that's gonna make you a golf professional."

*****

Standing on the first tee, Jitterbug and I met the other two aspiring golf professionals scheduled to play in my group. The first fellow, named Evan, had a great golf swing and wasted no time in sending a bullet down the middle of the first fairway.

The other young guy, Cameron, had taken the PAT on eleven previous occasions, missing by only two shots on his last attempt.

He said that near-miss actually encouraged him since only sixteen golfers in a field of seventy-four made it through.

We came out firing, but the rain started only moments after making the first turn. I was one under par after thirteen holes, but felt my driver slip on the fourteenth tee. I looked up in horror to see my tee shot fly over the white stakes guarding the right side.

Boom. Triple bogey. Two over par and the heavy rain had yet to take center stage.

I did the best I could to keep my grips dry and went through all of my handkerchiefs, wrapping the grip of my club before each shot. It worked well until the third hole of the second eighteen, when the rain became torrential.

I walked to the twenty-first hole of the day still two over par, but took a big swing, lost control and flung my driver into the ground. My popped up tee shot stayed in bounds, but knocked off fewer than sixty of the 425 yards.

"We should stop," I said. "They can't expect us to play in this!"

Nevertheless, we kept going, praying someone would postpone play.

Walking off the thirteenth green, my thirty-first hole of the day, I only had one shot to spare, which meant I could do no worse than a bogey and four pars on the way in. Evan, too, had one shot to spare and Cameron was right on the number, needing an even par finish on the remaining five holes to make the grade.

Approaching the fourteenth tee, we found ourselves in the company of scores of other participants. Although nobody had postponed the tournament, the players in front of us had all stopped in protest.

"It's about time we stop!" I said. "We shoulda quit a long time ago when we still had some shots left."

"What do you mean?" Jitterbug said. "You're just gonna quit because everyone else quit?"

There was something in Jitterbug's inflection when he said the word, "quit," I found unsettling, but thought, *Surely, whoever is leading this revolt knows what he's doing.*

Jitterbug approached Cameron, who was sitting in his cart, dejected as I. Smiling, he said, "You know, Cameron, I got an uncle who just passed away this past week. His name was Smiley. They called him Smiley 'cause he never smiled, but believe it or not, he liked his nickname."

Cameron listened attentively to Jitterbug.

"I remember the first time I saw Smiley play in a golf tournament. Oh, I couldn't have been more than about ten years old. Uncle Smiley went into the second round of a two-day tournament leading by a shot, but for some reason, couldn't get out of the box that day and made a ten on the first hole. That's right! He walked to the first tee with a one-stroke lead and to the second tee five shots behind.

"But, you know what? Uncle Smiley made six birdies on the way in and finished the day tied for first place. Unfortunately, he lost in the playoff, but can you believe it? Smiley started with a ten and still shot even par seventy-two!"

Jitterbug's smile faded as he continued. "You know, before and after that, Smiley shot sixty-threes, sixty-fours, and sixty-fives, but until the day he died if you asked him about his best round ever, he'd tell you it was the day he started with a ten on the first hole. Now, I don't know why Smiley felt that way. I mean, makin' that ten cost him the tournament!"

Jitterbug paused before giving Cameron a penetrating stare. "But, I think it's because on that day, instead of feeling sorry for himself, he stuck his chest out and didn't give up. I suspect when all is said and done, those kinda days are the only ones that mean anything."

Cameron, having hung on every word, nodded as he got out of his cart. He pulled the sopping wet cover off of his driver, sloshed through the maze of umbrellas and put his tee in the ground on the short par four fourteenth.

A player from another group said out loud, "Hey, we're all quitting. They should've called it off a long time ago."

Cameron didn't say a word. He had failed eleven times before and wasn't about to let another chance slide by.

Without looking up, Cameron lashed a tee shot down the right side, just inside the fairway. At that, Evan said, "We're back on, Bobby. Let's finish this thing."

Before we knew it, we were on the tee at the par five eighteenth. Unfortunately, Evan made a big number on seventeen and was completely out of it. Cameron and I were both on target, both needing par to make it.

The two of us played a game of follow-the-leader, both hitting a three-wood off the tee, five-iron down the middle of the drenched, narrow fairway, and another five-iron to the front of the green. We were side-by-side every step of the way.

Once on the green, we found my ball only fractionally closer than Cameron's, which meant I would watch his seventy-foot first attempt.

As soon as he stroked the putt, I knew it wouldn't get there. We all yelled, "Go! Go! Go!" but his ball pulled up some eighteen feet short of the hole.

Seeing this, I hit my putt with everything I had; barely got the ball to the hole, but left myself only six inches to shoot exactly 150. It felt like the weight of the world had been lifted. Even so, I couldn't yet breathe easily, as I hoped hard for Cameron to finally make it.

I tapped in, walked to the far edge of the green, and stood alone in the pouring rain. *Smiley, you've already given me the world, but there's just one more thing. Cameron really needs to make this putt. He hasn't said a cross word all day, and he's a good guy. He deserves this more than I do, Smiley.*

Cameron squared up to his putt with the face of a cat preparing to pounce. I looked across the green where Evan and Jitterbug shared an umbrella. Neither could look away from the scene unfolding on the eighteenth green.

Rain dripped from bill of Cameron's cap as he looked back and forth between his ball and the hole. I crossed my fingers. *Come on, Cameron, drive that thing home.*

Cameron banged his putt up the hill. We all cheered when Cameron's ball hit the back of the hole, jumped straight up, splashed down, and slowly sunk to the bottom of the cup.

Cameron's face fell into this hands.

*****

Two of us made the grade, but it was no time to celebrate. There was one man in our group who didn't fare as well. On our way to the scorer's booth, Jitterbug spoke from under his umbrella. "You three men have something to be proud of. It would have been easy to quit, but you finished."

He then turned to Evan. "Young man, you have a beautiful golf swing and you will pass this playing test. But that's for another day. Today, you did better than pass it. You stuck it out. I don't worry about guys who stick it out because they always find a way to get there."

Play was never officially suspended, so all who stopped in protest were disqualified. Seven of us, out of ninety-nine, passed.

Seek And Ye Shall Find

On the way home from Winston-Salem, riding in the passenger seat with Jitterbug at the wheel, reality began to knock at my consciousness. My rough six-year goal had been accomplished in just three years. I could start the three-year training program as soon as I was ready.

I should've been on top of the world, but was far from it. The words of Jessica's father played over and over in my head.

Pulling into the Muni parking lot, it occurred to me I hadn't properly expressed my appreciation. "Jitterbug, before I get in my truck and drive away I want you to know all the time and effort you put into me is the reason I passed the test today. You must know that already, but I want you to know I know it, too."

"Bobby, it wasn't anything at all."

"Yes, it was. You got up in the middle of the night to drive us two hours to Winston-Salem. Then, you walked around a rainy golf course for nearly ten hours, and just drove two hours back; you're still wet from head to toe, and this is just today. You've been going out of your way for me for two years. I'll never be able to repay you."

"Watching you has been good for me in ways you can't even imagine," Jitterbug said. "By the way, Mr. Vaughn is going to want to congratulate you in person. I happen to know he'll be here tomorrow. Any chance you can meet us in the pro shop at ten o'clock tomorrow morning?"

"Yeah, sure, of course."

"Good then," Jitterbug said. "And congratulations on what you accomplished. I bet you can't wait to call your father."

"You're right, I can't wait," I said. "He told me to call him no matter how late I get home. So, I'll call him, and then Mom, because Mom will keep me on the phone longer."

Jitterbug laughed. "So, call your parents tonight, and then what? What's the next big thing for you?"

"PGA School," I said. "And, I know I should be happy about that, but everything feels a little hollow right now. I feel like I'm about to lose Jessica. I'd gladly trade in today's accomplishment if it meant I could keep her forever."

"I know it seems tough right now, Bobby," Jitterbug said. "But, can I ask you a question?"

"Yeah."

"Do you love Jessica?"

"Do I love her? Yes, I do."

"Does Jessica love you?"

"She says she does."

Jitterbug turned off the engine and opened his car door. "Grab your putter, Bobby. Let's go over to the putting green and roll some balls."

"I'm afraid I'm all golfed out, Jitterbug," I said. "Besides, it's been dark for over an hour."

"There's a full moon. C'mon, I want to show you something." Jitterbug popped the trunk, walked to the back of his car and removed the putter from my golf bag. I followed him to the putting green where he handed me my Ping Anser and dropped three balls. "Take a look out there, Bobby."

I cast my gaze onto the putting green and was surprised to discover all six holes were visible. The partially revealing moonlight made it possible to putt. Never before had I considered night putting. Jitterbug pointed to a hole cut on the side of a keen slope some thirty feet away. "Give it your best roll."

I positioned my putter behind a ball, surveyed the terrain over which I intended to roll the putt, and gave it a firm stroke. The ball started some six feet left before taking the bend and crawling down to within a foot of the hole. "Wow, I almost made that," I said.

Jitterbug motioned for me to try again. The second putt traveled on about the same line as the first, and, once more, narrowly missed falling in. After three or four trips back and across the green, it was clear the dimly lit putting green provided plenty of light to both read the break and judge the distance. But, more amazing to me was how effortless the process of lining up and stroking the putt was. Somehow, putting seemed simpler on this scarcely illuminated practice green.

"Anything you find remarkable?" Jitterbug asked.

"Putting seems easier by the moonlight," I said. "I don't know how it could be, but it is."

Jitterbug walked in closer, slowly reached out, and removed the putter from my light grip. "It's because you're seeing the green the way you should always see the green. By the moonlight you can easily recognize the big, prominent breaks, but you're not distracted by the small ones. Bad putters are the guys who try to take into account every little break and bump they're afraid the ball might take. Seeking, and then finding, all the little imperfections does nothing except make the mind and muscles tight. Heartache comes when a guy loses appreciation for the big, important breaks, and chooses instead to focus on the small ones."

I thought about the sign above the workshop in Jitterbug's garage. ***Seek and ye shall find***

It was in this moment I finally understood the significance of those words. *It's not just the good things; it's the bad, too. Whatever you look for you will find. Roger didn't create the insecurity I feel. I created it. I expected him to find fault with me, so he did. Jessica is the big break. I need only keep my attention on her, and the rest of the world will line up with it. Seek and ye shall find.*

The enormity of the moment hit me in the face and tears swelled in my eyes. "Jitterbug, how could you have known?"

Jitterbug reached out and placed his two hands on my shoulders. "You've put in the work, Bobby. Now it's time you accept some of the reward for your efforts."

"But, I don't get it," I said. "You picked me. Why on earth did you pick me?"

Jitterbug shook his head. "You picked yourself, Bobby. Remember? You showed up. After that I just took my seat in the front row." Jitterbug lifted his hands, and brought his palms together for a single clap. "Now, it's time you get on out of here. I'll see you tomorrow morning at ten."

I wiped my eyes with the collar on my shirt. "Thank you again, Jitterbug. I'll see you in the morning."

*****

"Hello?"

"How is the most wonderful girl in the world on this beautiful night?"

"Oh my goodness, wait a minute," Jessica said. "Okay, I'm sitting. Tell me how it went."

"Jessica, what happened today doesn't matter. Everything is perfect because I have you."

Jessica laughed, and it was the most beautiful sound I'd ever heard. "Oh, wow," she said. "Don't let me interrupt you. Continue please."

"I want to spend all day with you tomorrow. Can I pick you up in the morning at 9:30? I just need to make a quick stop by Muni and then anything you want."

"Of course, but you're killing me! How did the PAT go?"

"Jessica, I passed, right on the number, but it wouldn't have mattered either way. I thought it did but it didn't. I have you and that's all I care..."

"You passed!!!! Oh my Gosh!! I knew you would! I'm so excited!!"

"Can I pick you up at 9:30 tomorrow morning?"

"Yes, I'll be ready! Oh my gosh, you passed!!!"

"You're wonderful, I'll see you in the morning."

The Reward

Holding the door for Jessica, she was already a step inside the pro shop when I happened to glance down to the tee box on the fourth hole. I remembered the first time I hit a shot there and how I sliced my drive into the creek on the right side. The memory made me smile. Turning to catch Jessica, my forward motion was interrupted by a sudden eruption of applause. There, shoulder to shoulder, spanning the entire width and half the depth of the pro shop, were Muni members, all with their hats off, smiling and clapping their hands. At the front of the pack, prominently positioned, was Mr. Vaughn. I couldn't have been more surprised, or more proud to have Jessica there to see it. The applause tapered off after just a few seconds. "Wow, a hats-off ovation," I said. "I've never heard of that before."

Mr. Vaughn looked up from his wheelchair. "The hats off are for the lady. And, you should show some respect and remove yours, too."

Embarrassed, I reached up to remove my visor. "I beg your pardon. It was a crime of thoughtlessness."

"You haven't blown it yet," Mr. Vaughn said. "You can still be a gentleman and introduce us to this lucky lady."

Jessica's radiant smile had the attention of every eye in the room. "Jessica, this is Mr. Vaughn."

"Pleased to meet you, Jessica," Mr. Vaughn said, holding his ball cap against the buttons on his shirt.

"Thank you, Mr. Vaughn. I've heard so much about you."

"And, this is Clayton Berry."

Jessica paused. "Do you mean, as in 'Lord' Berry?"

Uh-oh. I don't call him that to his face. "Well, that's not his actual name."

Lord Berry smiled as he reached out for Jessica's hand. "If you wish to call me Lord Berry, I will happily answer to it. It's a pleasure to meet you, Jessica. Charmed, really."

"And, this is Jitterbug."

Jitterbug lifted his hand, but it wouldn't be enough, as Jessica moved in for a hug. "I'm really sorry about your loss. I heard so much about Smiley, and am sad I never got to meet him."

The moment was stolen when Roger stood up from the seat he occupied at a small table adjacent to the pro shop counter. You could see in Jessica's face she didn't expect to see her father. "Dad? Oh my gosh, you're supposed to be at the lake. Why are you here?"

Roger hesitated, visibly uncomfortable with the spotlight. "I came to see Bobby," he said, catching my stare. "Uh, Bobby, may I have a moment of your time?"

Jitterbug spoke up before I could. "Go on, Bobby, I'll keep Jessica company while you step away. We'll be right here."

I followed Roger to a corner of the pro shop. "Bobby, it occurred to me I never expressed my appreciation for the gift you gave me. Thank you for the golf manuscript."

That was the last thing I expected Roger to say. "You're welcome. I wasn't sure if you even read it."

"I read it last night," Roger said. "I took it to the lake, and opened it up after Jessica called to tell us you passed your playing test. Three hours later I'd read the whole thing. I'm curious, Bobby, did you write that journal yourself?"

"I wrote it," I said. "But, I can't take credit for the lessons. They all came from that guy over there talking to your daughter. He taught me every lesson I wrote about in my journal."

"The lessons were good," Roger said. "But, so was the writing. All those rainy days at the library paid off. You taught yourself to write."

"That means a lot, Roger. Thank you."

"You're welcome. Anyway, I've been here for almost an hour now, and have gotten to know Stan Watkins, the gentleman over there behind the counter. I guess you could say I've learned a few things."

"You learned a few things? Like what?"

"Like about the wedge you had with you at Cambria. I had no idea that club belonged to a friend of yours who passed away. I want to apologize for the incident with Troy. It was inexcusable and I'm sorry."

"Roger, it's okay. There was no way for either of you..."

"Please, let me finish. It's not okay, and there is something else I learned from Stan today."

"What's that?"

"You may not remember the first time you came to our house for dinner, but it was last summer."

How could I forget? "Sure, I remember."

"We were discussing your future, and you changed the subject, like you didn't want to talk about it. I thought you were hiding something. What I didn't know then, but I learned from Stan to-day, is you're a little talker and a big doer. I don't know where you learned that, but it's an admirable combination of traits."

I motioned over to where Jessica stood. "Once again, it was that guy over there talking to your daughter. He told me the words of man who seems eager to talk about himself don't mean anything. I guess it was good advice."

Roger looked at Jitterbug, who shared a big smile with Jessica; both enjoying, at long last, their first introduction. "Yes, it was, Bobby. It was good advice. Anyway, I want you to know when I leave here this morning I'm going over to Cambria Country Club."

"Why? You playing golf?"

Roger shook his head. "No. I'm going to suspend my membership. I may go back some day, but Cambria is not a place I want to be right now."

"Why?"

"I could go into a number of reasons why, but suffice it to say it's not okay for me to be a member at a club where my own daughter doesn't feel comfortable."

"Oh, I don't think she cares. She just…"

"I care," Roger said. "And, by the way, Troy and I are not cut from the same cloth. It's important to me that you and Jessica both know that. He sponsored me so I could get into Cambria, and out of loyalty to him I treated you badly. I'm embarrassed and I apologize."

"You don't need to apologize to me," I said. "And, I mean, you're always welcome to play here at Muni, I guess you know that."

Roger smiled. "Thank you, Bobby. I can see you have a lot of friends here who care about you. I'd feel honored to get to know them."

"Why not now?" I said, turning to Jitterbug. "Excuse me, Harold?" Jitterbug looked up from his conversation with Jessica. "Yes, Harold, can you please come over here for a second?"

Jitterbug waved his hand in front, inviting Jessica to lead the walk over. "Harold Bell, this is Jessica's father, Dr. Roger Carrington."

"Glad to have you here, Dr. Carrington." The two shook hands.

"Please, call me Roger."

"Roger it is then."

Roger paused and stared at Jitterbug, as if trying to remember where he'd heard his name. "Are you the Harold Bell who won the North Carolina State Open?"

"Four times," I said.

Jitterbug shot me a quick glance, and shook his head before turning back to Roger. "You, sir, don't look old enough to remember that."

I had to interrupt. "Uh, yes, Harold, sorry to pull you away. Dr. Carrington and I were talking about the possibility of him acquiring a membership here at Muni, but he doesn't have a sponsor. Since I'm rather close to the family, it seems only appropriate I should step aside and let somebody else sign off on him. Do you think you could help him out?"

Jitterbug pretended to ponder the idea, and feigned frustration at the absence of an obvious solution. "Well shoot, I can't vouch for somebody I don't know. I mean it's my reputation I'd be putting on the line." Jitterbug stroked his chin as he looked down, then up, and finally snapped his fingers. "I think I got it," he said. "I suppose what's missing here is we really haven't gotten acquainted. We should get to know one another over a round of golf. Any chance you can meet me on the first tee at seven o'clock tomorrow morning?"

It took a moment, but a smile formed on Roger's face. "Yes sir, I can be here tomorrow morning."

Jitterbug reached out and wrapped his hand around the hand of Jessica's father. "And no more of this 'sir' stuff either," he said. "My friends call me Jitterbug. I'll see you bright and early."

Epilogue

I've thought about those words many times. "And, no more of this 'sir' stuff" must be Jitterbug's way of saying, "You're a friend of someone I care about, and that makes you my friend."

I don't play as much golf as I did in those early days at Muni. Heck, not many people do. Of course, I still love the game, and will forever jump at a chance to walk around Muni with Jitterbug, but Jessica is the most important thing in my life, and I'll never give her reason to doubt it.

I spend most of these days out on the golf course teaching others what I learned at Muni:

That you never leave the last person to putt with the job of picking up the flagstick.

That you don't cheer when your opponent misses a short putt to lose the match.

That how you play golf shows a little bit about your character; but how you lose at golf shows all of it.

That you only fail when you give up before it's over.

That you get what you focus on, no matter what.

That you can do anything you want, but not everything you want.

And, most importantly, that you show up. That amazing things happen to those who keep showing up.

I have some big shoes to fill. I can only hope to do as well.

Acknowledgements

I'd like to first acknowledge William (bil) Mannina for the inspiration his encouraging words provided. It's hard to know if this book would've gotten off the ground without bil's help. At the very least, it would've been a much different book, as so much of what bil shared involved the central message in *Jitterbug's Gift*.

The most difficult thing about being a golf writer is finding an editor who understands the game. How happy I was to find Barbara Orr. Not only did Barb provide proofreading services (what she initially signed up for), but offered a great deal with respect to content, plotlines, and things only a person familiar with both golf and writing could provide. Barb's help and guidance proved invaluable.

We all have that friend we've known so long we can't be upset by their criticism. That friend, to me, is Chip Ramey. Chip didn't pull any punches after reading this book's first draft. His honesty (at times, brutal) led to some significant, much needed changes.

I would like to acknowledge John Laubhan. John wrote one of my favorite books in the golf genre, entitled *Bogeymen*, a story so rich and full of character it was only natural I'd seek his advice. His suggestions were so simple, yet so important; I couldn't be more thankful for John's input.

I'd like to acknowledge a handful of people who read over the book before the final publication.

Beth Steiner, who in the end, described Jitterbug as someone "who wanted to give back to the game that had given him so much." I think she's on to something with that.

Bill Pelham, the author of the highly acclaimed, *Burke and Demaret*, which provided much inspiration for this book.

Jeff Edmundson, who has been a voice of support in just about everything I've done for the last ten years. Jeff is the kind of friend we all need in our lives.

A special thanks goes out to Terry Angel, James Kramer, and Jeff Jameson for the advice they provided.

I am more than thankful for my father, Bob Steiner, who patiently listened in as I read, and re-read, out loud nearly every line in *Jitterbug's Gift*. He would tell you he's done very little, but I see it differently.

And, one more before I close. I want to acknowledge Mr. Dave Rusk. I will always treasure the hundreds of rounds we played, just the two of us, over five seasons at The Golf Club at Little Turtle. Mr. Rusk extolled the virtues of hard work, of doing one's best, and the obligation one should feel to be honest. Mr. Rusk, one might assert, stood in for Jitterbug during a period in my life when I needed him. When you read the story, *Seek and Ye Shall Find*, I hope you will think of Mr. Rusk. He was the inspiration.

Order Form

Give the Gift of *Jitterbug's Gift*
To your Friends and Fellow Golfers
Go to BobbySteiner.com or order here:

I want ______ copies of *Jitterbug's Gift* for $19.95 each.
Include $6.45 Shipping and Handling for the first book, and $1.95 for each additional book.

Enclosed is a check or money order for $__________

❑ I am interested in having Bobby Steiner speak to my company or organization.

Name____

Organization__________________________________

Address______________________________________

City/State/Zip_________________________________

Phone_______________________________________

Email____

Please charge my credit card:

Card #_______________________________ Exp __________

Signature_____________________________________

Make check payable to and mail to:
Robert C Steiner
52-990 Avenida Rubio
La Quinta, CA 92253

Or for personalized books, email Bobby directly:
Bobby@BobbySteiner.com